Radiation and Reason

The Impact of Science on a Culture of Fear

Wade Allison

Published by

Wade Allison Publishing

Published as an e-book (June 2009)
ISBN 978-0-9562756-0-8
and in paperback (October 2009)
ISBN 0-9562756-1-3   978-0-9562756-1-5
Website http://www.radiationandreason.com
Printed and distributed by
York Publishing Services Ltd
64 Hallfield Road, Layerthorpe,
York, UK   YO31 7ZQ

Last saved 19 September 2009

For Alfie, Alice, Joss, Minnie
and those who come after,
may they understand one day.

About the author

Professor Wade Allison, MA DPhil, is a Fellow of Keble College and a Professor of Physics at the University of Oxford where he has studied and taught for over 40 years. His earlier research work was in elementary particle physics, in particular the radiation field of relativistic particles, but his interests and expertise have spread much wider. He recently published *Fundamental Physics for Probing and Imaging*, an advanced textbook for his course at Oxford on medical physics, including radiation and its use in clinical medicine and the wider environment. Of the safety of radiation and nuclear technology, he says

> *I have no axe to grind, I have no links with the industry, I just want to see the truth out there. So many people have been under a misapprehension for so long.*

Of the conclusions of this book he says

> *It brings good news – but are the people of the world ready to re-examine past assumptions in the light of current science? It is important that they do, because, without nuclear energy, the future for mankind looks bleak.*

Contents

Preface

The human race is in a dilemma; it is threatened by economic instability on one hand and by climate change on the other. Either of these could lead to widespread unrest and political turmoil, if the right choices are not made now. In particular, prosperity without carbon emission implies a comprehensive switch in our sources of energy. With luck, the activity generated by the process of switching will also contribute to prosperity in the short and medium term. There are many solutions – wind, tidal, solar, improved efficiency – but the most powerful and reliable source is nuclear. However, it is widely supposed that this presents a major problem of safety. Is this long-held concern about radiation and nuclear technology fully justified? Straightforward questions should have simple answers, and the simplest answer is *No*. Explaining and exploring the question and this answer in accessible terms is the subject of this book.

Over the years I have taught and studied many areas of physics, including nuclear physics and medical physics, although I have never had a close link with the nuclear industry. While it always seemed clear to me that radiation safety was somewhat alarmist and unbalanced, in earlier decades the apparent freedom to opt for fossil fuel as the primary source of energy meant that there was no special reason to confront public perceptions of the issue. But now the situation has changed, and it is time to address the whole question.

But how, and with what voice? A discussion in popular terms that would appeal to the native common sense of the reader is too easily dismissed by the science. But scientific answers are impenetrable to many readers, and so fall on deaf ears. A way forward is to vary the tone, sometimes scientific but still accessible, and sometimes with illustrations and examples that appeal to general experience. Nevertheless, I shall probably tax each reader's tolerance in places, one way or the other, and for that I apologise. While ways of avoiding the use of equations have been found except in some footnotes, use is made of the scientific notation for very large and small numbers.[1] Finding passages that seem either trivial or impenetrable, the reader is encouraged to skip forward to rejoin further on. The passages that discuss recent scientific results are supported with references labelled in square brackets in the text and listed in full at the back. Most references may be found on the Web at the address given – but the text is self-contained and does not suppose that these are consulted. Also at the back, there is a short list of books and papers, headed *Further Reading*.

The story starts with the physical science, much of which has been established for decades – the atmosphere, the atomic nucleus and radiation. And then it moves on to the effect of radiation in biology, most of which was not so well known 30 years ago. Often, popular science is written to amaze and inspire – and that is important. But here the target is more prosaic and practical, namely a clear understanding of the scientific background to some of the threats and decisions that are likely to determine our environment and thence our survival. The central question is this: how significant are the health risks due to radiation and nuclear technology? In Chapters 6 and 7 the current evidence is shown with the relevant ideas in modern biology. Not all questions can be answered completely yet, but they can be answered quite well enough. The conclusions are rather surprising, and do not match well with currently enforced radiation safety levels. This challenge by modern radio-biology to radiation safety regulation is well aired in scientific papers, but has not been explained to the community at large, who have a significant interest in the matter. The costs of nuclear technology are very high, in part because of the exceptional radiation safety provision that is made. Scaling back such provision by a large factor would have a major beneficial effect on the financial viability of an extensive nuclear power programme.

---

[1]   Thus 10^6 means one million, 1 followed by six noughts. Similarly 10^{-6} means one millionth part.

These scientific findings do not depend on climate change, although that is what makes the question important at this time. But why, in the past, did most of the human race come to hold extreme views about the dangers of radiation and nuclear technology? The last part of the book describes what nuclear technology now offers, a large-scale supply of carbon-free electric power, with further options for the supply of food and fresh water.

E M Forster wrote

> *I suggest that the only books that influence us are those for which we are ready, and which have gone a little farther down our particular path than we have yet gone ourselves.*

I hope that for some readers the message of this book is timely.

To keep the discussion focussed on a few main points, many important topics have been omitted or just noted in passing – in particular, the subject of micro-dosimetry is treated rather briefly, in spite of its importance for future understanding. No doubt mistakes have been made too, and credit not given where it was due. Such choices, mistakes and lapses are mine, and I apologise for them.

I have benefited from conversations with many colleagues during the writing of this book. It has been a privilege to have had the opportunity for quiet reflection and study, undisturbed by the pursuit of grant funding that distorts so much academic study today. This work would not have reached fruition without the contributions of many people. Former students and members of their families, members of my own family too, have spent long hours, reading and providing feedback on my efforts to produce an accessible account. In particular, I should like to thank Martin Lyons, Mark Germain, James Hollow, Geoff Hollow, Paul Neate, Rachel Allen, John Mulvey and John Priestland for their reading of the text and important comments. Chris Gibson and Jack Simmons have provided me with invaluable comment and information. Throughout, I have relied heavily on the encouragement of Elizabeth Jackson and my wife, Kate – their

4   Preface

advice and persistence were essential. I thank Kate and all members of my family for their love and tolerance over the past three years while I have been rather absorbed.

Finally I would like to thank Paul Simpson of LynkIT and Cathi Poole of YPS for their enthusiastic ideas and *can do* reaction to the task of printing and promoting this book and its message.

Wade Allison,

Oxford,

September 2009

Chapter 1 Perceptions

Science is the great antidote to the poison of enthusiasm and superstition.

Adam Smith, economist (1723–1790)

A mistake

Radiation is seen as a cause for exceptional concern and alarm, though few people have any personal experience of its dangers. Is this view justified, and how did it come to be held?

Prior to the Second World War there was a degree of relaxed public acceptance of radiation, principally because few knew anything to suggest otherwise. That changed with the arrival of the Nuclear Age.

The destruction of the Japanese cities of Hiroshima and Nagasaki by nuclear bombs in 1945 was a military and political success that avoided a land invasion of Japan, which would have been immensely costly in lives for both sides. As a technical scientific enterprise, it was a triumph – no project depending on fundamentally new physical developments on such a scale had ever been attempted before.

As an exercise in the public understanding of science, it was a disaster whose consequences still persist. The message that came through was very clear – what happened was both extraordinarily dangerous, and incomprehensible to all but a few. The extreme apprehension generated in the population was self-sustaining. Sources of fear inhibit free enquiry, and few in the population ever questioned the extent of the danger. In the decades of the Cold War that followed, this fear was a useful weapon in international politics, and its basis was not doubted, even by those in a position to do so. And then there was Chernobyl – a further failure of public understanding. In the public mind the fear of nuclear war had infected views on civil nuclear power.

Most people simply wanted to distance themselves from anything nuclear.

More questions should have been asked, although some of the answers could not have been given in earlier decades. There are three concentric concerns, related like the layers of an onion, as it were. The first and innermost is to understand the effect of radiation on human life. This is a scientific question, not dependent on the other two. The second task is to educate public opinion and formulate safety regimes in the light of the solution to the scientific question. The final problem is to discourage nation states and terrorists from exploiting radiation as a source of fear by threatening and posturing. This depends critically on the second task, establishing robust public opinion and a regulation regime that can face up to international arm twisting.

In the last 50 years these problems have been confused. During the Cold War era, international politics exploited public fear and ignorance of radiation, while only recently has the scientific evidence and understanding become established to answer the prior scientific question. In the absence of a clear picture of the biology and of adequate human-based evidence, radiation safety guidelines and legislation became established on a reactive basis. Public concerns were handled by imposing draconian regulation on radiation and nuclear technology, in the expectation that this would provide the necessary reassurance. But the very severity of the restraints only increased public alarm and people were not reassured.

But now in the new century there have been two changes. Firstly, the scientific answers that were lacking previously are now largely available. Secondly, new nuclear power plants are urgently needed so that the use of fossil fuel can be reduced – this does not change the safety of radiation but it does affect the importance of setting matters right as soon as possible. So the purpose of this book is to explain the science in fairly accessible terms, together with some of the evidence, and to offer a rough but justified estimate of the level of new safety regulation.

Consequences for public policy and international diplomacy may then follow.

Personal risk and knowledge

Making decisions to reduce the risk of accidents involves everybody in society, what they believe to be the level of risk, as well as what is actually the level of risk. People may be alarmed, when they do not need to be – they may be fearless, when they should be more cautious.

What level of risk is tolerable in exceptional circumstances? We should not say zero – a risk-free society is utopian and unachievable. Although personal fear may feel absolute and unquantifiable, it should be controlled – any risks involved should be compared with those of alternative courses of action. Even the duration of life on Earth will have its term, hopefully not caused by early escalating climate change. But for us as individuals, the end is closer and more certain, for finally we all die – life expectancy may be 70 to 80 years, depending on standard of living, health and diet. So what is the average effect on a life of an accident that carries a 1% risk of death? For an average age of 40, that means a life expectancy reduced by an average of 0.4 years, or 5 months. If the lifelong risk is 0.1%, the reduction in life expectancy is just 2 weeks. This is at the same level as many risks and choices that people incur as they go about their daily lives. Many people would, willingly, give up 2 weeks of life for the benefit of their children or grandchildren if that would really benefit the large-scale prospect for the planet. Well, wouldn't they? So, thinking straight, a lifetime risk of death at the level of one in a thousand is sensible – if undertaken for good reason, of course. As we shall see, the evidence shows that only under quite exceptional conditions is any nuclear risk at such a high level.

In general, those who make decisions need to be sure that they themselves understand the relevant situation. If their information is picked up from others on the basis of a collective idea that *everybody knows*, there is a chance that wrong decisions will be made. The greater the number of people relying on the opinion of others, the longer it takes for them to realise if something is wrong. So, the bigger a blind spot in understanding, the greater the chance that basic questions go unasked and unanswered. At a practical level, a hard question may be beyond the immediate field of an individual – and so be passed to an expert for a specialised opinion, perhaps without reference to other problems. In this way the true picture may become distorted in the form of a collection of separate narrowly defined opinions.

An example was the flow of intelligence and decision-making in the conduct of the First World War. A consequence was the extreme loss of life, for example, on the Somme in July 1916. Decisions on the course of action were taken by commanders, who did not know or appreciate the actual situation in the field. And those on the battlefield were not permitted to use their own intelligence to modify the plan. It was assumed that the heaviest possible artillery bombardment would destroy the barbed wire and overcome the machine-gun posts – but it did not. The commanders did not find out, and the men on the ground were required to obey instructions. The result was an avoidable massacre.

A more recent example was the effect on the stability of the world financial system of various trading and insurance practices employed in the first few years of the 21st century. Financial regulators and senior managers of corporations, who, in the years leading up to 2008, encouraged their dealers to negotiate and exchange contracts of risk for money, were not able to grasp the instability of the structures that they were building. These were described as *complex* and *sophisticated* – words that should themselves be a warning. Used to impress, they invite acceptance without question. When the financial structures collapsed, nobody was able to determine the ownership and the worth of their holdings. The absence of anyone with the ability to see the consequences of what was happening was as serious as on the Somme in 1916. The financial dislocation, which played a dramatic part in the collapse of 2008, was foreseen eight years earlier by Wilmott [1], who wrote as follows.

The once 'gentlemanly' business of finance has become a game for 'players'. These players are increasingly technically sophisticated, typically having PhDs in a numerate discipline. ... Unfortunately, as the mathematics of finance reaches higher levels so the level of common sense seems to drop. ... It is clear that a major rethink is desperately required if the world is to avoid a mathematician-led market meltdown.

When decisions are scientific, the availability of adequate first-hand understanding can be a major hurdle, because such understanding is sparse in the population. This is especially true for decisions involving nuclear radiation. To the general population and those who make decisions for society, the words and ideas that describe the science do not have familiar meanings. Apprehension of anything nuclear, or concerned with radiation, is deeply engrained in popular culture, and few scientists have pursued the broader inter-disciplinary field.

For reasonable decision-making, it is essential that the truth underlying the fears of nuclear material and radiation are properly exposed and that the science is more widely understood. This is more urgent now because new dangers affect the survival of the environment as a whole, not just the lives of individuals.

Individual and collective opinions

Should decisions on major dangers be made individually or collectively? Many creatures concentrate on collective survival at the expense of the individual – the herd or the swarm comes first. But man is different – he places special value on the importance of individual rights, as well as the collective agreements that are essential to society and its survival. This dynamic relationship between individuals and society is what being human is about. But what happens if a collective understanding takes a wrong turn, leading to a consensus that threatens survival? Then the problem needs to be re-examined, which is most difficult if it is largely scientific.

What people understand of the world depends on their previous experience, including education and upbringing. Even what they think that they see is shaped and filtered by their background. Through the character of the Professor in his children's book, *The Lion, the Witch and the Wardrobe*, C S Lewis advises that we should listen to evidence from others, assess their reliability and sanity, and then await further developments. Recent scientific reports [2] relate how, even today, the experience of our own bodies can be distorted alarmingly by suggestion and supposition, in a way dating back to ancient witchcraft. In modern physics, too, there are serious questions concerning reality in its different manifestations [3].

So reality is tricky. It is not just an academic matter for philosophers, but a practical matter that is the source of everyday disagreements. If differing views are reconciled, plans of action can then be agreed and decisions taken that lead to success and increased confidence. So, decisions need an acceptable collective picture of reality, and this only becomes established through repeated observations at different times and by different people, and is confirmed when expectations based on it turn out to be correct. This is most credible when scientific observations are found to confirm precise mathematical predictions – although we cannot account for the unreasonable relevance of such mathematics in the world. There is no logic that requires that, when I wake tomorrow morning, the world as I know it will still be there. A chicken, accustomed to being fed by the farmer each morning, is unprepared for his day of slaughter, although that was the ultimate purpose of each morning feed.[2] So we become accustomed to the continuity and predictability of our experience. But could it be otherwise? We need always to be alert to the possibility that our collective understanding is quite wrong. It is the task of the following chapters to try to unpick the

---

[2] Remarked by Bertrand Russell.

dangers of radiation and nuclear technology and to explain how we were previously mistaken.

Philosophers and physicists may mull over evidence for the existence of parallel streams of reality. Some may follow the ideas of Descartes by looking at which properties of the Universe are necessary, simply to allow us to be here now asking questions. This is called the *Anthropic Principle* and it turns out to have significant consequences, if you accept its premise. But our task is different, though related in a practical and local sense. We are re-opening our attitude to radiation and nuclear technology in order to help answer the larger question: what kind of world and choice of life style will permit the possibility that mankind will be here in the future to ask questions? This local anthropic prospective is also restrictive. If no solution is found, human life on Earth as we know it will die out.

Confidence and decisions

Consider an example. In earlier centuries exploration and the transport of people and goods depended on the confidence and safety of navigation. Observations and sightings had to be agreed, a ship's course calculated and steered – the arrival of the ship at its destination was the demonstration that these decisions were not just matters of opinion. The calculation of the position of the ship relied on measurements and the known apparent orbits of the Sun, Moon and stars, the magnetic field of the Earth, the tides and other quantities. With every improvement in navigation came an uplift in world communication; better accuracy gave improved confidence, leading to more ambitious voyages and better trading. Conversely, whenever confidence in the natural world fails, human activity gets choked off and prosperity declines.

If there is disagreement, the observations and preconceptions have to be talked through to reach a consensus. But it is an important concession to the variety of human experience that individuals have the right of choice. Except when it is unavoidable, we do not exercise choice on behalf of others – and then only with a degree of caution that we would not exercise for ourselves. And so it is in matters of safety, especially where apprehension is high.

The dangers of radiation and nuclear technology have been a matter of vocal public concern for half a century, mainly among the currently middle-aged and elderly who remain confused and apprehensive. The younger generation never experienced the Cold War and are more relaxed. In the past many scientists kept away from the long-running debate of nuclear politics. Meanwhile, radiation safety remains subject to exceptionally stringent conditions, although few people appreciate the related expense and no one seems to feel safer as a result. In the 21st century the agenda has changed and decisions are needed for the future of the environment where the choice of primary energy source is between nuclear power with the dangers of its waste and the combustion of fossil fuel with its waste.

Science and safety

The astronomer who first predicted an eclipse and announced it to the political masters of his day discovered the influence that scientific knowledge can bring. His ability was held in awe by all around him. Today physics and astronomy have given the human race control over much of the natural world. In earlier times and in the absence of scientific interpretation, darkness, fog, thunder, lightning and other variations in nature tended to generate superstition and thoughts of divine intervention, even punishment. Such feelings suppress confidence and discourage initiative and enterprise.

The scientific enlightenment from the 17th to mid 20th centuries showed man how to overcome fear of the unknown by empirical study. Through universal education, training and communication this encouraged prosperity and better standards of living and health. However, misapprehension of the natural world is still the background of life for many.

Scientists, too, suffer misapprehensions, but these are overcome by continual re-measurement, re-thinking and re-calculation, like the helmsman steering the wrong course who, by making further observations, discovers and corrects his error. If this is not done, confidence may fail and unguided imagination and panic fill its place. Then careful observation and calm thought are at risk, and the opportunity to correct errors is reduced.

This is particularly true for those dangers that cannot be sensed. The prospect of a threat, unseen but lethal, makes people worry, even panic. Trivially, in the dark, when sources of danger cannot be seen, people can be frightened until the light is turned on. This case is instructive – to give people confidence they need to see for themselves using a basic instrument, like a flashlight or torch. Just telling them that they should not be frightened is not effective. Equally, consulting people for their opinion about safety, when they do not know or understand, may simply accelerate an implosion of confidence – decisions taken in everybody's best interest cannot emerge in this way. Regulation and legal restraint do not give people confidence either. Only real education of a sizeable fraction of the community can reassure, and this should be based on an objective understanding of the issues.

For the confidence of those on board, the ship should be on the right course, and be known to be on the right course. The two aspects of safety – actual and apparent – are different, though equally important. Once actual safety has been established, apparent safety becomes a matter for education, communication and information. If an appearance of safety is given priority over actual safety, real danger can follow, as reassured passengers on board the Titanic learned to their cost.

Chapter 2 Atmospheric Environment

Size and composition of the atmosphere

The environment comprises the Earth's crust, the oceans and the atmosphere. The depth of the crust that affects us on a regular basis is between a few hundred and perhaps a thousand metres, and the oceans have a similar mass. But the atmosphere is much smaller − although it reaches to an effective height of about 10,000 metres, its density is a thousand times less than water. So it is equivalent to a layer of water on the Earth just 10 metres thick − less than 1% of the mass of the oceans or the Earth's crust. So it is easily polluted and, being composed of gas, any pollution is quickly dispersed into the whole.

The composition of the atmosphere today is 78% nitrogen, 20% oxygen and 1% argon with smaller amounts of carbon dioxide and water vapour. Oxygen and water are fiercely reactive but nitrogen, carbon dioxide and argon are less reactive or totally un-reactive. Until two and a half billion years ago there was little atmospheric oxygen. Its concentration was increased by photosynthesis in early plant life powered by the Sun. This break-up of carbon dioxide into free oxygen and carboniferous plant life 'charged the battery' for all life processes. Oxygen remains a powerful chemical, not only when this battery is discharged in the burning of plant matter, fossilised or not, but also in related oxidative processes in living cells. These may be benign, as in the oxidation of sugars that provides the energy for living creatures; they may also be malign, as when oxidation disrupts cellular processes and leads to cancer. Fortunately life has evolved ways in which to protect itself against such oxygen damage that are effective most of the time. Coincidentally, these same protection mechanisms turn out to be equally effective against the damage caused by radiation, as we shall see later.

Atmospheric change

The average surface temperature of the Earth is critically dependent on the composition of the atmosphere, and a small release of pollution can have a relatively large effect on the climate. The reason for this is explored in Chapter 4 in terms of the spectrum of thermal radiation absorbed and emitted by the Earth. Pollution released into the oceans would also have an environmental effect, but a much diluted one that would not impact directly on the temperature. In the case of the Earth's crust dangerous materials – suitably buried – can stay put for many millions of years. So care of the environment is concerned first and foremost with the atmosphere.

Since man started to employ fire and organised agriculture to raise his standard of living, he has released an increasing mass of contaminants into the atmosphere, although only recently has the extent of their effect been appreciated.

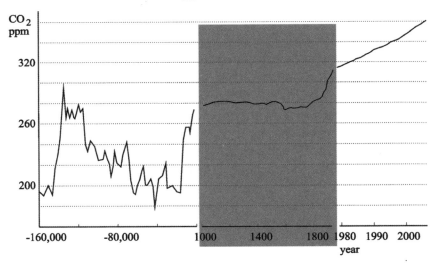

Figure 1 The concentration of carbon dioxide in the atmosphere for three separate epochs. Left: prehistoric variation (measured from Antarctic ice cores). Centre: historic data (also from ice cores). Right: modern measurements (direct from the atmosphere).

For example, the growth in the concentration of carbon dioxide in the atmosphere is shown in Figure 1. The left part of the diagram shows the concentration for most of the past 160,000 years, going up and down within the range 200–280 parts per million (ppm) and spanning various states of the world's ice sheets. The central part of the plot shows that it was fairly constant at 280 ppm from 1000 AD until the industrial revolution, with its rapid increase in population and pollution. Since then it has risen remorselessly as shown on the right – the latest data say that it has risen by 40 ppm in 25 years and currently stands at 360 ppm. Note the large change in timescale for the three parts of the plot.

A plot for methane would show a similar rapid increase. These effects come from the increased burning of fossil fuels and the destruction of forests, exacerbated by the rising world population of humans and animals. These gases are called greenhouse gases because they have the effect of causing a rise in the average world temperature, as explained in Chapter 4. The temperature change is expected to be self-reinforcing for several reasons whose relative importance is still uncertain.

Firstly, the water vapour in the atmosphere naturally increases as the air gets warmer, and, since water vapour is also a greenhouse gas (as explained later on page 39), it is expected to contribute a further rise in temperature.

Secondly, as the temperature rises the extent of the polar ice caps is reduced, and, without the reflection of the snow and ice, the surface of the Earth becomes darker to sunlight. The extra solar absorption in polar regions is responsible for another increase in the surface temperature.

Thirdly, as the temperature rises, plant material that was previously preserved and locked in the 'deep freeze' of the permafrost starts to rot and decompose, emitting further greenhouse gases, specifically methane.

Any increased incidence of forest fires accompanying the temperature rise releases yet more gases. As living plant life absorbs carbon dioxide and releases oxygen, any reduction in forestation is harmful on both counts. The re-absorption of carbon dioxide from the atmosphere by sea water and through plant growth is slow. In fact, on average, it takes about a hundred years for any carbon dioxide, once released, to be re-absorbed. So, even if all emissions were stopped immediately, climate change would continue for a century or so before possibly stabilising. If emissions continue, the climate will continue to change. The population that the world can support may be reduced and, as deserts expand, large migrations of people towards more temperate regions may be expected. To reduce greenhouse gas emission, other ways of providing sufficient energy and food for the world population must be found, and all available solutions pursued simultaneously.

Much energy can be saved with care and by investment in new technology, for example efficient power supplies and LEDs (light-emitting diodes). For the energy production itself, wind, tidal, solar, geothermal and hydroelectric sources provide electric power without gas emission. Each is appropriate to a particular kind of locality. Some are intermittent, some are expensive and many are limited in scale. Intermittent sources need to be coupled with energy storage, but there are no easy options there. Energy for transport also needs storage, but battery technology and hydrogen storage have significant limitations.

Energy and agriculture

Increased populations with rising standards of living expect more fresh water and food. The shift from a basic, mainly vegetarian, diet to a regular meat-eating lifestyle requires more water. But the extra water consumption of ruminants and their added gas releases are both significant. Meanwhile many parts of the world suffer increased desertification and depletion of ground water supplies. Unlimited clean water can be obtained from sea water by the process of desalination but this requires significant amounts of energy.

Much food goes to waste though traditionally its deterioration may be reduced by refrigeration, but this also requires energy, both to power the refrigeration and to transport the refrigeration units. Alternatively food may be preserved by irradiation, a method that requires no ongoing energy supply but is little used. Food waste and an affluent diet increase the demand for more agricultural land, which leads in turn to further deforestation.

These observations motivate a re-examination of society's attitude towards radiation and the nuclear option, as the major source of energy for almost all purposes.

The word energy is used frequently in the following chapters and it might be helpful to explain what it means. Energy is measured in joules, and 100 joules of energy is what it takes to power a 100 watt light bulb for 1 second. Energy is conserved – that means it does not get lost – and it is inter-convertible between different forms, to some extent. Forms of energy include heat, sunlight, chemical, nuclear, electrical, hydro and many others.

In a waterfall the same quantity of energy may be carried by a large mass of water that drops a small height, or a smaller mass of water that drops through a larger height. But the difference can be important. There is a similar distinction between nuclear and fossil fuel energy sources. The same total energy may come from a small number of atoms each releasing a large energy, or a large number of atoms (or molecules) releasing a small energy. The former is what happens in a nuclear power station and the latter in a fossil fuel one. Usually in the following chapters the word energy will refer to the energy per atom. It should be understood that many, many atoms may deliver much energy, but the amount of fuel required and the waste generated for each joule produced increases if the energy per atom is small.

This energy per atom is five million times smaller for fossil fuel than for nuclear, as explained in footnote 6 on page 29. So, for the same amount of electricity, the amount of fossil fuel required (with its waste) is five million times the amount of nuclear fuel (with its waste). This is the crux of the story.

Chapter 3 The Atomic Nucleus

His enormous head bristled with red hair; between his shoulders was an enormous hump...
The feet were huge; the hands monstrous. Yet with all that deformity was a certain fearsome appearance of vigour, agility and courage...
'It's Quasimodo, the bell ringer. Let all pregnant women beware!' cried the students.
'...Oh that hideous ape! ... As wicked as he is ugly ...it's the devil.'
The women hid their faces.

Victor Hugo, writer (1802–1885)

Powerful and beneficial

In his novel, *The Hunchback of Notre Dame*, Victor Hugo introduces the central figure with these words. While the citizens of mediaeval Paris are repelled by his ugliness and afraid of his strength, no one cares to discover his true nature. As the story unfolds, Quasimodo reveals a natural gentleness and kindness towards Esmeralda, the beautiful gypsy girl, who is condemned to death on the gallows. The people's fear prevents them from appreciating him until he uses his strength in the attempt to save Esmeralda's life.

Such is the public image of radiation. Like Quasimodo, it is seen as ugly, strong and dangerous. Like him it engenders an almost universal reaction of fear and rejection. Many do not want to be near anything to do with radiation or even to understand such things. This is unfortunate, because the human race has survived through the power of thought and understanding. The suspension of that power is not good news for the future.

The following descriptive but scientifically robust account shows how radiation and the atomic nucleus fit into the natural physical world.

Size scales

The stage on which the science of radiation, radioactivity and fundamental life processes is set requires a broad range of scales – very small distances as well as larger ones, and very small energies and much larger ones too. Despite their differences these distances and energies are inter-related through fundamental science.

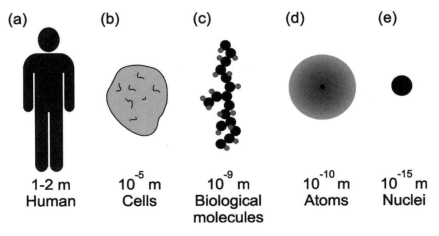

(a)	(b)	(c)	(d)	(e)
1-2 m	10^{-5} m	10^{-9} m	10^{-10} m	10^{-15} m
Human	Cells	Biological molecules	Atoms	Nuclei

Figure 2 The scales of the different structures relevant to the interaction of radiation with life, from man through cells, molecules and atoms to nuclei.

Figure 2 gives an idea of these spatial scales, starting from a human on the scale of a metre, Figure 2a. Roughly speaking the biological structure of each human is realised in the form of a large ensemble of cells, each on a scale of about 10^{-5} metres, Figure 2b, although some cells are very much smaller and some larger. This means that some are just about visible with the naked eye but for many a microscope is needed. Cells vary as much in function as in size. Each is composed of about 70% water and a large number of biological molecules.

Figure 2c is a sketch of a section of a biological molecule – typically these form long chains that fold up within cells. Such are the working proteins and the double-helical DNA that holds the genetic records. Each molecule is a particular sequence of chemical atoms. Simple diatomic molecules, like the oxygen and nitrogen in the atmosphere, have just two atoms. The polyatomic ones, like carbon dioxide, methane and water, have three or more, so that they can stretch, turn and wriggle about – which gives them their greenhouse gas properties. Big biological molecules are composed of hundreds of thousands of atoms.

Whereas there is a multitude of different molecules, there are only a small number of different types of atom. The information and variety of molecules lies in the arrangement of these atoms and their chemical connections. Biological molecules are composed of hydrogen, carbon, nitrogen and oxygen atoms only, with special additional roles for calcium, phosphorus, sodium and potassium. Within less than a factor two all atoms have the same size, about 10^{-10} metres across. In other words, each atom is as about 100,000 times smaller than a typical cell, roughly the same factor by which a cell is smaller than a man.

Figure 2d shows an atom as made of a tiny nucleus surrounded by a cloud of electrons. The number of electrons in this cloud is known as the atomic number Z and this alone determines the atom's chemical behaviour – the nucleus with a balancing charge Ze makes the atom electrically neutral overall but takes no part in the 'social' behaviour between atoms. This is because the scale of the nucleus is 100,000 times smaller than the atom itself, coincidentally the same ratio as an average cell is to a man and as an atom to an average cell. All types of nuclei are of a similar size, about 10^{-15} metres across.

What do we know about these atoms and nuclei, and how were they discovered?

Atoms and electrons

To the eye and to the touch most materials are smooth and continuous. A few are grainy but the grains vary and are not fundamental in any sense. Only the occurrence of crystals with their highly regular facets gives a clue of hidden structure. But that was not why the Greeks, Leucippus and Democritus, suggested that matter is composed of atoms. Their arguments were not really based on observation at all, it seems. They were simply unhappy in principle that matter should be indefinitely divisible. Based on such a vague argument, perhaps it is not surprising that the atomic idea fell into disfavour in classical times, not least because Aristotle was not impressed by it.

Only at the start of the 19th century did the atomic theory reappear, this time to account for observations. These were that the proportions of pure chemicals taking part in reactions, burning for example, are related by simple whole numbers. Altogether there are over 90 different types of atom – the elements. These atoms themselves do not change – changes to their mutual groupings are all that is needed for a simplified account of chemistry. As these patterns change, the stored energy may increase or decrease, and when this energy is released, the material becomes hotter.

Some chemical changes do not happen unless the atoms are hot in the first place. This can lead to a runaway process, in that, the hotter the material becomes, the more heat is released. This is the unstable process that we all know as fire, a chain reaction that is often highly destructive. It was an early and crucial stage in human development when man learnt how to control fire, to use it for warmth and to cook with it. He came to accept its risks in exchange for the better life that it brought. Even today much expense is incurred in protecting against its dangers and many still die every year through fire accidents. In spite of this no civilisation has banned fire on safety grounds – it is too valuable a technology to lose.

But there are lessons that early man did not learn about fire. The waste products are solid ash and gas, predominantly carbon dioxide and water vapour, released into the atmosphere. Once in the atmosphere, if the temperature is sufficiently low, the water condenses out in a few hours or days in the form of rain, but the carbon dioxide persists. Only now has mankind started to appreciate the danger of releasing the waste of this chain reaction. Unfortunately he did not understand this when he first started making use of fire in prehistoric times.

But it was discovered that there is more to the behaviour of atoms than simply rearranging them to make different molecules. Towards the end of the 19th century with advances in glass and vacuum technology it became possible to make sealed glass tubes of low pressure gas through which electric currents could be passed between metal electrodes if one of these was heated. These currents emit light and this technology is the basis of the sodium and mercury lights commonly used in street lighting, the neon tube used in signs, and energy-saving fluorescent tubes. If fully evacuated, such a tube is called a cathode ray tube – familiar today as an old TV tube, now largely replaced by flat panel displays. In the science laboratory two early fundamental physics discoveries were made with such tubes.

Firstly, the current, as it passes through a cathode ray tube, is composed of a stream of charged particles of very small mass. Remarkably these electrical particles are of the same type, whatever the atomic composition of the electrodes or gas. These particles, present in all atoms, are electrons, a new universal particle discovered in 1897 by J J Thompson. In a TV tube the picture is 'painted' by a beam of these electrons striking the inside of the front face of the tube and lighting up the different coloured phosphors there.

Secondly, if these electrons are given enough energy and then strike a metal plate, invisible uncharged radiation is emitted. These X-rays were found to be electrically neutral and highly penetrating, unlike the parent electron beam. This discovery was made by Röntgen in 1895. Very quickly the value of the penetrating power of this radiation was appreciated for medical imaging and therapy. The relationship between electrons, atoms and the electrically charged ions, as they appear in the workings of electric cells and batteries, was explained – ions are formed when an uncharged atom gains or loses one or more electrons.

However, knocking such small parts off an atom – an electron forms less than one thousandth of the weight of an atom – did not reveal much about the composition or structure of the rest of the atom. There was more to be discovered, deeper within.

The nuclear atom

The first evidence of activity inside the atom, beyond the addition or loss of electrons, came with the discovery of radioactivity in 1896 by Henri Becquerel, whose work was followed later by the discoveries made by Pierre and Marie Curie.[3] They found that all chemical salts of certain heavy elements emitted radiation and that this energy was not dependent on the ionised state of these elements, or on their physical and chemical state. Evidently the energy was coming from the deeper inner atom and not from the surrounding electrons. Through careful work the Curies showed that chemical elements were being transformed, so that new ones appeared whenever an atomic nucleus emitted radiation connected with its radioactivity. Three types of this radiation were identified, alpha, beta and gamma – quite often in physics discoveries are given such enigmatic names, because, initially at least, not enough is known to name them in terms of their true characteristics. Later it was shown that alpha, beta and gamma radiation are in fact streams of helium ions, electrons and electromagnetic radiation[4], respectively.

Radioactive atoms are very unusual and heavy – the implications for the structure of ordinary elements that are not radioactive were quite unclear initially. Some years later Ernest Rutherford showed by experiment that, for every atom, all of the mass (except for the electrons) and all the balancing positive charge are concentrated in a tiny volume at the centre of the atom – the nucleus. With its surrounding atomic electrons, this is the atom

---

[3] The discoveries of 1895, 1896 and 1897 were so unexpected and came in such short succession that less careful experimenters felt encouraged to come forward with claims based on fantasy. In particular the magical powers attributed to so-called *N rays* were only shown to be false after much publicity.

[4] Described in Chapter 4.

as we understand it today. The arrangement has been compared with the Sun and its solar system of planets. But this is deceptive – the proportions are wrong. The Sun is a thousand times smaller than the solar system while the nucleus is a hundred thousand times smaller than the atom. Seen from the edge of the atom, the nucleus would be far too small to be seen with the naked eye – if, for a moment, you can imagine yourself on such a scale. The rest of the atom is quite empty apart from the thin cloud of electrons.

Since the 1920s quantum mechanics, the radical shift in our understanding of the physical world, has explained in full precisely why molecules, atoms and nuclei have the structure and behaviour that they do. Recently, as computers have become faster, it has been possible to extend such explanations and predictions to the properties of larger and larger chemical and biological molecules.

For reasons explained below, nuclear change is very energetic compared with chemical change and it powers the Sun upon which life depends. Earlier in the history of the Universe all the chemical elements were formed by nuclear change from the primordial hydrogen and helium that remained after the Big Bang. However, since the Earth was formed roughly six thousand million years ago, only one nucleus in a million has undergone any change at all. Within a small range all materials are 99.975% nuclear by weight – electrons only account for 0.025%. So nuclear material is very common but substantial nuclear change is quite remarkably rare.

In the early 1930s it was shown that every nucleus is composed of a certain number of protons and neutrons. The proton is the positively charged nucleus of simple hydrogen, and the neutron is its uncharged counterpart. The proton and neutron are almost identical in size and weight, and their properties differ only on account of electrical charge. Elements are characterised by their chemistry – that is by the number of surrounding electrons. This is the same as the characteristic number of protons to ensure electrical neutrality. However, a given element may exist in several forms called isotopes – the only difference between these is the number of neutrons each contains. Apart from the variation in mass, different isotopes behave identically, except on the rare occasions when nuclear change is involved. They are named by their element and then their atomic mass number A – this is just the total number of protons and neutrons that each contains. Examples are uranium-235, lead-208 and oxygen-16.

Whereas the number of neutrons that an atom contains has little influence on its external behaviour, the internal structure and stability of the atomic nucleus are significantly affected, including whether it rotates. In fact each element has only a small number of isotopes, of which only a few are stable. Most unstable ones have decayed away long ago and are no longer to be found in nature. If a nucleus rotates, it behaves like a tiny magnet.[5] In a large magnetic field these rotating nuclei tend to line up like iron filings or compass needles. Their alignment can be controlled and measured using radio-waves without invoking any nuclear change. This is called nuclear magnetic resonance (NMR) and is the basis of magnetic resonance imaging (MRI). In clinical use the description nuclear has been dropped from the name, in deference to the risk of worry that this label might cause! In fact the magnetic energy of a nucleus in MRI is about one millionth of a typical chemical energy.

On the other hand the typical energy of a proton or neutron inside a nucleus is large – about a million times larger than the energy of an electron inside an atom, that is normal chemical energy. The reason for this is a universal basic feature of quantum mechanics. The simple two-line calculation given in footnote 6 at the bottom of the next page gives a factor of about five million. This ratio does not change much if calculated more precisely and sets the scale of the enhancement of nuclear energy over chemical energy. So roughly speaking, a nuclear power station gives a million times as much energy per kilogram of fuel, and per kilogram of waste, as a fossil fuel power station delivering the same electrical energy.

---

[5] Every rotating charge behaves as a magnet – this is a universal relationship. Conversely, all magnets are due to rotating or circulating charge.

The quiescent nucleus

Each nucleus remains really rather isolated at the centre of its atom. Other than flipping its spin under the influence of radio-waves, as in MRI, it can do nothing. It may be moved passively within its deep shield of surrounding electrons, but only as an inert mass. What prevents it taking a more active role? There are several reasons for this remoteness.

Like the electrons the behaviour of a nucleus within an atom is described by quantum mechanics – in both cases there are only a certain number of states that can be occupied. For the electrons these states are not far separated in energy. As a result atoms change electronic state frequently, emitting or absorbing light and generally taking part in chemical or electrical activity. But nuclei cannot do this because the separation of their states is typically five million times greater.[6] So nuclei are effectively 'frozen' into their lowest state unless extreme energy is available.

The second reason for the remoteness of the nucleus is that the electrons ignore it, except through the electrical attraction. As a result the electrons on the one hand and the protons and neutrons on the other keep their own company and the nuclear core remains separated at the atomic centre.

Even if nuclei do not interact with electrons much, why do they not interact with each other? Actually this is not possible because, being all highly positively charged, they are kept well apart by their strong mutual electrical repulsion. This acts like a

---

[6] In quantum mechanics a proton or electron of mass m contained in a region of size ℓ must have a momentum P of about $\hbar/\ell$, where $\hbar$ is Planck's constant. In simple mechanics, for a mass m with velocity v, there is a relation between the momentum $P = mv$ and the kinetic energy $E = \frac{1}{2}mv^2$. So that

$$E = P^2/2m = \hbar^2/(2m\ell^2).$$

Using this formula we can compare the energy of an electron in an atom with that of a proton or neutron in a nucleus. The ratio of the size of the region ℓ is 100,000; the ratio of mass m is 1/2000. The formula tells us that typical nuclear energies are larger than atomic (that is chemical) energies by the ratio of $m\ell^2$, that is about 5 million.

powerful spring between them and it takes enormous energy to drive them close enough together to touch, effectively.

Nuclei are not excited when illuminated by beams of radiation either, unless the energy of the radiation is quite exceptionally high or the radiation is composed of neutrons. If the radiation is a beam of protons or alpha particles, these are repelled before they ever get close to any nucleus. A beam of electrons or electromagnetic radiation is equally ineffective because these do not react with nuclei except electrically, as just discussed. The only way in which the outside world can effect any change in a nucleus is through collision with a neutron. Having no electrical charge, neutrons are not repelled and can enter a nucleus with ease. But free neutrons are unstable, decaying with a half-life[7] of 15 minutes, and so their presence in the natural environment is exceptional.

If the influence of the environment on a nucleus is very rare, how about the other way around? When do nuclei affect the environment? On its own, all that a nucleus can do is decay, if it is unstable, thereby releasing a certain energy into the environment. Most naturally occurring nuclei are stable and cannot do this. For the handful of naturally occurring nuclei that do decay, the process is very slow and rare, and this is why unstable nuclei were not discovered until 1896. Most varieties of nuclei that could decay, already did so within a few million years of being formed, more than six thousand million years ago.

When a nucleus decays, the total energy of the emitted radiation and the residual nucleus (including its mass) must equal the total energy of the initial nucleus (including its mass). This is because in a decay no energy is lost – and no electric charge is lost either.

---

[7]   In a group of neutrons the decay of any particular one occurs quite randomly in time – except that each can decay only once. So the number that remain falls naturally with time, and consequently so does the rate at which these decay. If the time for half of the nuclei to decay is T (called the *half-life*), then the number left is reduced by a further factor of a half with every successive time interval T. This is called an exponential decay and describes any unstable atom and nucleus.

The same is true for the atomic mass number A, the sum of the number of neutrons plus protons, that is $N+Z$. The total A present before the decay equals the combined number afterwards.[8] Table 1 explains how the alpha, beta and gamma decays first studied by the Curies match with these rules.

Table 1   The usual types of natural radioactivity, alpha, beta and gamma, where N and Z are the numbers of neutrons and protons in the initial nucleus.

Type	Residual nucleus			Radiation	
	Neutrons	Protons	Charge	Form	Charge
Alpha	$N-2$	$Z-2$	$Z-2$	helium nucleus	+2
Beta	$N-1$	$Z+1$	$Z+1$	electron	−1
Gamma	N	Z	Z	electromagnetic	0

In alpha decay both N and Z of the residual nucleus decrease by two and an alpha particle, a helium ion composed of the four nucleons, is emitted. In beta decay a neutron becomes a proton with emission of an electron to balance electric charge. There is a second type of beta decay in which a proton is changed into a neutron and a positive anti-electron (or positron) – such decays are of great importance in nuclear medicine. Actually in all types of beta decay another particle is emitted too. It is called the neutrino. But we are not interested in neutrino radiation in this context because it effectively disappears, without depositing any energy or doing any damage.[9]

In fission decay the nucleus splits into two fairly equal halves with the emission of a few extra neutrons. Such decays are exceedingly rare 'in the wild', even for radioactive isotopes,

---

[8] The rules for charge and energy conservation are deeply embedded in the principles of physics, although the rule for A is empirical.

[9] Neutrinos interact so seldom that they can pass right through the Sun or the Earth, although after 50 years of experiments they are now well understood.

which are themselves rare. However, in the artificial circumstance in which a nucleus has just absorbed a neutron, fission can occur efficiently and quickly. This induced fission process requires a flux of such neutrons – for instance inside a fission reactor. Each fission releases further neutrons that may then be absorbed by other nuclei, thus building up a neutron-induced chain reaction. This is like a chemical fire which is stimulated by its own heat production. A difference in the nuclear case is that remarkably few materials are 'combustible', as it were, and the 'fire' is very difficult to ignite.

Energy for the Sun

The Sun provides the energy that drives all aspects of life and the environment. Without the energy of the Sun, the Earth's surface would cool towards minus 270ºC, the temperature of inter-stellar space. Only the dull heat of the radioactive energy released within the Earth would raise the temperature at all.

Viewed over geological periods, fossil fuels act as chemical batteries that absorb the Sun's energy in one geological period and then give it back in another. The problem for mankind is that these batteries, charged over millions of years, are being discharged on the timescale of a century.

It is no surprise that the Sun was worshipped as a god in ancient times as the source of heat and light – a rather sensible choice of deity. An important question is, where does the Sun gets its energy? If this came from a chemical fire, it would have run out of fuel after about 5,000 years, but it has been shining for a million times longer than that already. The Sun is made of hydrogen and a small quantity of the element helium.[10] However,

---

[10] The name, helium, comes from the Greek name for the Sun. It is scarce on Earth but abundant in the Sun where its presence was first discovered. It is a very light gas that escapes upwards in the atmosphere on Earth – indeed it is used to fill fairground and party balloons for that reason. Fortunately plentiful supplies of helium for these and other uses come from the emission of alpha radiation in the decay of naturally radioactive atoms in the rocks of the Earth's crust.

there is no air or oxygen with which to support chemical combustion of the hydrogen.

The source of the Sun's energy is nuclear – it is a large reactor in which hydrogen 'burns' by fusion to form helium. The increase in energy relative to a chemical fire will enable the Sun to shine for many more thousand million years yet. This fusion reaction can only happen in the centre of the Sun where the temperature reaches several million degrees. Just as a chemical fire has to be started by a source of heat to get the reaction going, so to ignite a nuclear fusion fire, the hydrogen atoms must be given enough energy that, when they collide head-on, the nuclei can fuse together. At lower temperatures they simply bounce off one another without touching because of their mutual electrical repulsion. The visible surface of the Sun is at 5,800°C but the temperature rises with depth, and towards the centre it gets hot enough for this fusion to occur, a process that is now well understood. The energy released near the centre then finds its way slowly outwards towards the solar surface.

The Sun burns 600 million tons of hydrogen every second and yields 596 million tons of helium in its place. This curious loss of mass is balanced by the energy that streams out in all directions, such as towards the Earth. The rate at which the Sun loses energy E is related to the rate at which it loses mass m, the four million tons per second, by the equation $E = mc^2$ where c is the velocity of light. It is sometimes suggested that nuclear physics has a special connection with Einstein's Theory of Relativity, but this is not true – energy of all kinds is connected to mass in this way. One kilogram of mass is equivalent to 9×10^{16} Joules, or about 2×10^{10} kilowatt-hours. This is so large that it is only in the nuclear case that the mass change is noticeable. In the case of hydrogen fusing to helium it is just under 1%. This vast solar energy flux spreads as it radiates away. By the time it reaches the radius of the Earth's orbit it is a pleasantly warm 1.3 kilowatts per square metre.

Pleasant, maybe, but such a nuclear energy source deserves to be respected by modern man, as it was by the ancients. It is unwise to lie out in its radiation for long periods. However, the majority of people take a sensible attitude, enjoying a modest exposure without expecting that the risk of sunburn or skin cancer can be completely eliminated. By applying ultraviolet blocking cream and by limiting the duration of exposure, the warmth of sunshine at longer wavelengths may be enjoyed. No one seeks absolute safety from the Sun's rays – otherwise summer vacations taken in total darkness deep under ground would be keenly sought after! As with fire, mankind has learnt to live with the Sun, enjoying its benefits and avoiding its hazards. In both cases straightforward education and simple rules play their part. A similar measured attitude to other kinds of radiation would be beneficial.

Chapter 4 Ionising Radiation

The spectrum of radiation

So what exactly is radiation? The simplest answer is that it is energy on the move – and there are many kinds. Sunshine, music and waves on the surface of water are examples. At low levels many are quite harmless and even beneficial to life. Extreme levels can cause damage in almost every case – very loud music can damage hearing, and too much sun causes sunburn. However, a little sunshine is positively good for the skin by promoting the production of important vitamins. Similarly music that is not too loud may be positive and uplifting.

There is an important point here. It is not that gentle music causes only a little damage, but that it causes no damage to hearing whatever. When compared with the damage due to excessively loud sounds, the effect is not proportionate. Technically such a relationship is termed *non-linear* and this will be an important idea in subsequent chapters. In the case of music and damage to hearing the non-linearity may be obvious, but for other forms of radiation the distinction between proportionate and non-proportionate response will need to be looked at using both experimental data and an understanding of what is happening.

Most of the radiation from the Sun comes in the form of electromagnetic waves – this includes light and other parts of a wide spectrum. Each such wave involves entwined electric and magnetic fields. It has a frequency and an intensity just as a sound wave has a pitch and a volume. Our understanding of electromagnetic waves dates from the work of James Clerk-Maxwell in the 19th century, who built on the work of Michael Faraday and others. As for any wave, the speed at which it moves is equal to the frequency times the wavelength. Since the speed is essentially constant, the wave may be labelled by its wavelength instead of its frequency, but either will do. On a radio receiver, for example, some stations are labelled by their frequency in MHz (mega-hertz, millions of waves per second), while for others the wavelength in metres is used. The product of the two is the speed of radio-waves, 300 million metres per second, the same as that of light.

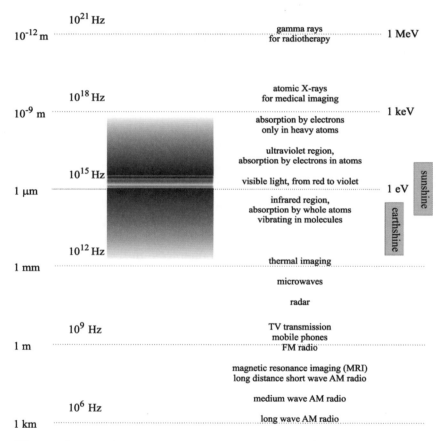

Figure 3 The frequency spectrum of electromagnetic waves.

How a wave is received is determined largely by the frequency not the intensity. For example, a radio receiver selects a station by choosing its frequency rather than its loudness. In the same way that for sound there are frequencies that cannot be heard by the ear, so for light there are frequencies that are invisible to the eye. In fact only a tiny range of frequencies of electromagnetic waves is visible. The whole spectrum is represented in Figure 3 with a logarithmic frequency scale running up the page and covering more than 15 powers of 10, as shown in the second column in oscillations per second (Hz). The first column gives the corresponding wavelength. Visible light with its characteristic spectrum of rainbow colours is the narrow band half way up the diagram. The point is that there really is no fundamental difference between these waves, from radio through light to X-rays, except the frequency. At the highest frequencies (and shortest wavelengths) the powers of 10 become harder to cope with and a third scale based on the electron volt (eV) is often used.[11] This is shown on the right of Figure 3 with the usual prefixes for powers of 10.[12]

Much benefit has been brought to everyday life through enabling mankind effectively to see using these other frequencies [4]. Lower in the diagram are radio-waves up to 10^9 Hz, used for example in MRI to see inside the human body and in radar to see ships and planes in fog and darkness. Slightly higher is thermal imaging, used to see warm bodies accidentally buried or concealed. Just below the visible frequencies is a region called the *infrared absorption band,* shown as shaded in the diagram. At these frequencies many materials are opaque because the rotation and vibration of molecules are in tune and resonate with electromagnetic waves. Above the visible there is another band, the *ultraviolet absorption band.* Here it is the more nimble atomic electrons that are in tune and the cause of the absorption. So here too materials are opaque, as marked by the shading.

Heavier elements with their more tightly bound electrons have an ultraviolet absorption band that extends to much higher

---

[11] The electron volt is 1.6×10^{-19} joules. This is a useful scale in the atom. The electron in the hydrogen atom has an energy of 13.6 eV while typical nuclear energies are in MeV.

[12] μ or micro, one millionth.   m or milli, one thousandth.
k or kilo, one thousand.   M or mega, one million.   G or giga, one billion.

frequencies than light elements. This is the frequency range of the X-rays. Here, metals like copper and calcium absorb radiation whereas carbon, hydrogen and oxygen are transparent. Medical images of a patient's teeth or bones (calcium) illuminated with such radiation show clearly any fracture or disease because the enveloping tissue (carbon, hydrogen and oxygen) is transparent.

Above about 100 keV atomic electrons, even those that are most tightly bound in the heavier elements, cannot move fast enough to follow the oscillating wave.[13] Consequently there is no resonance and all materials are largely transparent. This region is called the gamma ray region. Historically the distinction between X-rays and gamma rays depended on the source – electrons and nuclei, respectively. This distinction is deceptive because their effect does not depend on the source, only on their energy (or frequency). Today this switch of name is usually made at about 100 keV, but the distinction is really only a convention. Gamma rays are very penetrating, being only weakly absorbed, which is why they are used in radiotherapy to target energy into a cancer tumour, deep within a patient's body. This energy may then be absorbed in the tumour with sufficient intensity that its cells are killed and it ceases to function. There are practical difficulties in doing this, as discussed later in Chapter 7.

Damage from radiation

So understanding light, and then learning to see with radiation in other parts of the spectrum, is really useful. But what of the risks? The spectrum can be divided roughly into two halves separated at about 10 eV. Radiation of greater frequency or energy is called *ionising radiation*, that below, *non-ionising radiation*. The distinction is that ionising radiation can ionise and

---

[13] At such high frequencies the radiation appears less like waves and more like rays, or particles. In quantum mechanics this distinction has no real substance, and electromagnetic waves of any frequency f come in bundles of energy called *photons*, $E = hf$, where h is Planck's Constant. Each atom or nucleus emits one such bundle or particle when it decays.

break molecules apart – this is the radiation with which this book is primarily concerned.

Public concern about weak levels of non-ionising radiation, for instance from overhead power lines or mobile phones, is misplaced. The only known way in which such radiation can cause damage is by heating.[14] Put briefly, these radiation sources are safe if heat is not sensed – even then, benefits may dominate over any reasonable risk. Warmth from sunshine or a domestic fire is brought by the same kind of radiation as that in a microwave oven. While the radiation levels in such an oven can certainly be dangerous, the heat radiated by a glowing fire on a cold winter's day is a quite acceptable source of radiation hazard for most people – in spite of the fact that its heat level can be sensed, indeed because of it.

But non-ionising radiation still has a crucial environmental impact. On the right hand side of Figure 3 are two boxes labelled *sunshine* and *earthshine*. Very hot materials like the Sun emit light in the visible region, but cooler materials also emit, though predominantly in the infrared frequency range. The sunshine box indicates the range of frequencies that the Sun emits. Because this is centred on the visible region for which the atmosphere is largely transparent, much of this radiation reaches the surface of the Earth for the benefit of all, including plant life. (Actually the spectrum of the Sun extends a bit into the infrared and ultraviolet, too – the infrared part provides warmth, the ultraviolet causes sunburn, if not filtered by barrier cream and the small concentration of ozone present in the upper atmosphere.) The earthshine box indicates the frequency band of radiation that the surface of the Earth emits with its lower temperature – but not all of this radiation succeeds in getting out of the atmosphere because of infrared absorption by polyatomic

---

[14] This important statement can be scrutinised but the effect of radio-waves and microwaves on living tissue is well understood and they are widely used. For instance, they are used in MRI, safely below the level at which any significant heating occurs.

gases,[15] in particular carbon dioxide, water vapour and methane. With an atmosphere containing more of these the Earth is not able to cool itself nearly as effectively as it is able to absorb the sunshine. So energy is trapped in the atmosphere and the temperature increases. Crudely, this is how the *Greenhouse Effect* works. If the concentration of these gases rises, the Earth gets hotter and the climate changes. An extraordinary example is close at hand – Venus has a surface temperature of 460°C, thanks in part to an atmosphere with 97% carbon dioxide.

Like electromagnetic waves, beams of charged particles such as alpha and beta radiation can also damage molecules, so that they are classified as ionising radiation – and beams of neutrons and other ions too, although these are less common in the natural environment.

Nuclear stability

But what makes a nucleus decay? Or rather, what holds it together in the first place? The mutual electrical repulsion of the protons makes large nuclei more unstable than small ones. Stability only comes from the nuclear force that attracts neighbouring protons and neutrons together. This nuclear force overwhelms the electrical repulsion, but only at short distances within about 10^{-15} metres. As a result it favours small nuclei for which the protons and neutrons can huddle close together. The result is a balance between the preferences for nuclei to be not too large and not too small, which gives rise to the nuclear stability curve, Figure 4. The most stable atoms are those with nuclei at the highest point on the curve, the tightest average binding. These are in the region of iron, $A = 56$.

While quantum mechanics prefers nuclei with roughly equal numbers of protons and neutrons, the disruptive electrical force makes nuclei with too many protons unstable. The result is that

---

[15] Molecules like oxygen and nitrogen with just two atoms each do not vibrate and rotate with the same readiness that most polyatomic molecules do with all their many modes of internal movement. So they do not absorb much.

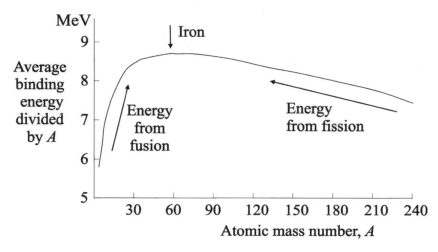

Figure 4 The average binding energy per proton or neutron as it depends on the atomic mass number, A.

all stable nuclei, except the largest, have roughly equal numbers of protons and neutrons, so that iron ($Z = 26$) has 30 neutrons. As shown in Figure 4, for smaller values of A the binding effect of the nuclear force is reduced; at larger values of A the disruptive influence of the electrical effect is increased – either way the binding is less. Above iron the compromise favours nuclei with more neutrons than protons because the disruption only acts on the protons. So for example, the most abundant isotope of lead, lead-208, has 82 protons but 126 neutrons. There are no naturally occurring elements above uranium ($Z = 92$) – those above actinium ($Z = 89$) are collectively referred to as the actinides.

The curve shows that in principle nuclei with small A could fuse together to release energy due to the nuclear force, as shown by the arrow on the left. This is nuclear fusion and the source of stellar energy, including that of the Sun. In addition, nuclei with large A can in principle release energy by splitting apart and moving towards greater stability as shown by the arrow on the

right. This is nuclear fission.[16] Because, like lead, the parent
nucleus has more extra neutrons than its stable fission products,
there are excess free neutrons emitted in the fission process. The
liberation of these extra neutrons is crucial to the nuclear chain
reaction mechanism.

In practice fission is very rare. Alpha decay in which a heavy
nucleus splits into helium and a smaller nucleus is more
common. This is the source of much of the natural radioactive
energy in the Earth's crust – the energy source of natural
geothermal power, in fact. In alpha decay nuclear energy is
released by moving to the left along the curve in steps of four
units in A. As A reduces, the excess proportion of neutrons has
also to be reduced, and this occurs by beta decay in which a
neutron in the nucleus decays emitting an electron and leaving
behind an extra proton within the nucleus.

**Table 2   The four distinct primordial radioactive series with
their head members and half-lives ($T_{1/2}$), and also end
members. $T_{1/2}$ is given in G-year, a thousand million years.**

	$4n$ series	$4n{+}1$ series	$4n{+}2$ series	$4n{+}3$ series
Head	thorium-232	neptunium-237	uranium-238	uranium-235
$T_{1/2}$	14.1 G-year	0.002 G-year	4.5 G-year	0.70 G-year
End	lead-208	bismuth-209	lead-206	lead-207

The natural radioactivity of heavy nuclei consists of a sequence
of alpha and beta decays in which energy is released as the
nucleus moves to lower A along the stability curve (Figure 4).
There are four distinct series of nuclei, depending on whether A
is of the form $4n$, $4n{+}1$, $4n{+}2$, or $4n{+}3$, where n is a whole
number. Within each series nuclei may decay, one into another,
by alpha or beta decay. Each series has a long-lived primordial
head member and an end member which is effectively stable –

---

[16] It is curious to note that in nuclear fission it is stored *electrical* energy that
is released. Energy due to strong nuclear binding is absorbed, not released, in
the fission process.

these are given in Table 2. The $4n+1$ neptunium series has already died out, but the other three are still active in the natural environment. The successive members of the $4n+2$ series, with their decays and half-lives, are shown in Table 3, as an example.

Table 3   Members of the uranium-238 series (the $A = 4n+2$ series). Some half-lives are measured in thousands of years (k-year).

Element-A	Z	N	Decay	Half-life
uranium-238	92	146	alpha	4.5 G-year
thorium-234	90	144	beta	24.1 day
proactinium-234	91	143	beta	1.17 minute
uranium-234	92	142	alpha	240 k-year
thorium-230	90	140	alpha	77 k-year
radium-226	88	138	alpha	1.6 k-year
radon-222	86	136	alpha	3.82 day
polonium-218	84	134	alpha	3.05 minute
lead-214	82	132	beta	26.8 minute
bismuth-214	83	131	beta	19.8 minute
polonium-214	84	130	alpha	164 microsecond
lead-210	82	128	beta	22.3 year
bismuth-210	83	127	beta	5.01 day
polonium-210	84	126	alpha	138.4 day
lead-206	82	124		metastable

Measuring radiation

To speak usefully of the effect on human life of different doses of ionising radiation, these must be measured, somehow. But how exactly?

The first step in quantifying a radiation exposure is to measure how much energy is absorbed per kilogram of living tissue during the exposure. This energy may cause chemical damage by breaking molecules apart that leads to biological (cellular) damage and finally to clinical damage, such as cancer or other disease. Such clinical damage turns out to be more difficult to relate to the exposure, especially as it may manifest itself in different ways, and on long or short timescales, from days to years.

In earlier decades knowledge of cell biology was too primitive to provide confident understanding, and adequate evidence of the effect of radiation on humans was not available to corroborate any particular view. In their absence, and for lack of anything better, the knowledge gap was bridged by a rule of thumb – a model in science-speak. This is the *Linear No-Threshold* model, abbreviated LNT. This assumes that clinical damage is in simple proportion to the initial radiation energy dose. No justification was given for it, but it was a reasonable working hypothesis at the time. Despite the poor state of knowledge, a start had to be made somewhere.

However, given modern biological knowledge and extensive records of human data, this model is now redundant and many of its more cautious implications can be ignored. The details are for discussion in later chapters. First, we return to the questions of the quantification of radioactivity and absorption of radiation energy in materials.

The rate at which energy is emitted by a radioactive source depends on the number of radioactive nuclei N, the energy of the decay, and the half-life T of the nucleus. The value of N is reduced by half with every successive time interval T and the average activity is proportional to N/T. Activity is measured in decays per second, called becquerel and abbreviated Bq. Sometimes the activity may be measured in a cubic metre of material, thus Bq m^{-3}.

So what does this mean in practice? Contamination by radioactive nuclei with a short half-life results in high activity for a short time; the same contamination with a longer half-life results in a lower activity, but it continues for longer. Half-life values vary between a small fraction of a second and many times the age of the Earth. So sources of radioactive contamination with short half-lives fade away while others with longer half-lives continue on. This is in contrast to most chemical pollutants, such as heavy metals like mercury or arsenic, that remain hazardous indefinitely. A slightly different situation arises when a dose of ionising radiation energy comes from an external beam produced by an accelerator (such as an X-ray machine) or from an external radioactive source.

Either way the important question is, how far does the radiation travel in material before being absorbed? Some radiation is so strongly absorbed in air, or any thin material, that it never reaches human tissue unless the source is on the skin or inside the body. Other radiation is weakly absorbed and can pass through the body. So what is important is not the intensity of the radiation, but the amount that is absorbed, for instance, per kilogram of tissue.[17] The extent to which it is absorbed depends on the kind of radiation and its energy (or frequency).

Alpha radiation is stopped even by air, and so the decay energy is deposited very close to the site of the radioactive contamination itself, with no dose at all only a little further away. An example is the energetic, but short range, alpha radiation emitted by the decay of the radioactive isotope polonium-210. A large internal dose of this was used allegedly by Russian agents to kill Alexander Litvinenko in London in 2006. No energy

---

[17] Radiation that just passes through and does not deposit any energy is necessarily harmless – like the neutrino radiation mentioned on page 31.

escaped the immediate location of the poison but there the tissue received the full radiation energy dose.

Beta decay produces electrons that travel further in material and, therefore, the deposited energy dose is more diffusely distributed around the radioactive source. Gamma rays go further still. So for a radioactive source in rock, for example, any alpha and most beta radiation is absorbed internally within the rock, and only the gamma radiation escapes to give an external energy deposition. In general a deposited energy dose is quantified as the number of joules of energy absorbed per kilogram of material, such as patient tissue. One joule per kilogram is called a gray (Gy). Typically doses are measured in milligray, with a milligray (mGy) being one thousandth part of a gray.

The clinical damage caused to living tissue by this deposited radiation develops as a result of a number of steps.
1.   The immediate molecular mayhem left by the radiation.
2.   Biological damage in which living cells are put out of action – this changes with time as the tissue responds to the radiation dose.
3.   The incidence of cancer (and other possible delayed or heritable effects) related to the exposure, perhaps decades later.
4.   The reduction in life expectancy as a result of such cancers (this effect on life expectancy is called the *radiation detriment* of the exposure).
5.   The chance of death shortly after exposure due to acute radiation sickness brought on by cell death and the shutdown of the normal biological cycle in one or more vital organs.

The two lasting consequences for life are described by the sequences 1-2-3-4 and 1-2-5, and later we will discuss how each of these outcomes relates to the initial radiation energy dose.

There are other causes of cancer, unrelated to radiation. Some causes – we shall refer to them generally as stresses – are natural, others are imposed by choice of lifestyle. Following decades of study much is known about how these stresses are related to the occurrence of cancer – to the detriment in fact. An important question is how the outcome is influenced when there is more than one stress. These stresses may be quite independent, as in smoking and radiation, but the result may not be. There remain some unanswered questions. But the point is that the range of residual uncertainty is too small to prevent mankind from taking decisions now about how radiation can be used with effective safety.

For a single acute dose the damage is related to the size of the dose and the type of radiation. The effects of X-rays, γ-rays and electrons are found to be roughly the same for the same energy dose in milligray. However, for other types of ionising radiation the biological damage is different. Quantitatively, the measured ratio of damage relative to X-rays is called the relative biological effectiveness (RBE). So the RBE of a radiation dose indicates how much more clinical damage it causes than is caused by the same number of milligray of energetic gamma rays. Essentially these RBE factors are measured quantities.

RBE factors vary with the clinical end point – that is with the cancer or disease concerned. Timing effects are important and we look at these later. The variation with radiation type is particularly interesting although not too large. For most practical applications of radiation safety, which we are thinking about in this discussion, we need to watch the factors of ten, a hundred and a thousand. RBE factors close to one are less important. Only in radiotherapy are the effects of radiation very finely balanced – but in that case gamma rays are usually used and so RBE is 1.0 anyway. So for this simplified discussion it is sensible to ignore the RBE factor in the first instance.

Nevertheless the International Commission for Radiological Protection (ICRP) has felt it necessary to include RBE in some way. In their radiation safety standards they multiply each energy dose in gray by a weighting factor, w_R, which plays the role of a broad-brush averaged RBE. [They define w_R for protons to be two; for alpha, fission fragments and other heavy ions to be 20; for neutrons it depends on the energy; for electrons and photons it is just one, by definition.] The result they define to be the *equivalent dose*, measured in units of sievert (Sv) – or millisievert (mSv). In ignoring RBE initially we treat doses measured in milligray and millisievert as equivalent, and come back later to the distinction when a variation in the type of radiation has something special to say about how radiation damage occurs.

These measures of energy deposited (and equivalent dose) may be for a single acute exposure. It is observed that cell damage is different if the dose is spread over a period of time, either as a series of repeated exposures, or as a continuous chronic rate of exposure. The question is why? What is the radiation detriment resulting from a chronic rather than an acute radiation exposure? How does the effect of a single dose of so-and-so many milligray compare with the effect of a continuous dose rate of a number of milligray per day – or per year? The matter is not simple, because dose and dose rate are quite different measures. This is the subject of Chapter 7.

Natural environment

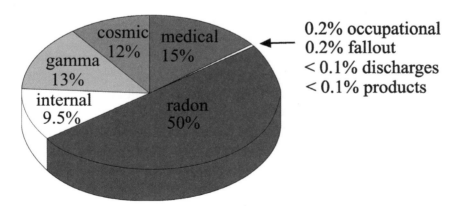

Figure 5 Origins of the average annual radiation exposure of the UK population, total 2.7 millisievert per year [5].

The radiation dose rate experienced by the population of the UK varies from one place to another. The average is 2.7 millisievert per year, and a breakdown of this radiation by source is summarised in Figure 5.

The slice labelled *cosmic* is for radiation that originates from space. The *radon* and *gamma* slices describe natural radioactive sources in nearby materials such as water, soil and rock. The *internal* radiation slice relates to the decay of radioactive atoms that occur naturally within the human body. The artificial part of the exposure is predominantly medical – the average due to all other man-made sources amounts to less than 0.5%.

The ionising radiation incident on the Earth from space is made up of electromagnetic radiation, protons and electrons. Some of the charged particle radiation comes from the Sun where the erupting magnetic fields of sunspots act as accelerators. At the top of the atmosphere this radiation causes ionisation, and the resulting discharges may be seen as the *Northern Lights* or aurora. Charged particles with low energy are deflected by the Earth's magnetic field, except in the magnetic polar regions, which is why the aurora are seen there. The resulting increased ionisation of the upper atmosphere affects satellite and radio communications, and when there is a magnetic storm this ionisation is high. None of these phenomena has any effect on health and the ionisation radiation does not reach the ground.

Cosmic radiation also includes protons that are more energetic and come from outside the solar system, and even outside the galaxy. These suffer nuclear collisions in the upper atmosphere. Some collisions create neutrons that then hit nitrogen nuclei high in the atmosphere to form the famous isotope, carbon-14. Although only 7.5 kg is created in total in the atmosphere each year, this is sufficient to maintain the proportion of carbon-14 in the natural biosphere (1 part in 10^{12}), which provides the basis of radiocarbon dating. This isotope decays with a half-life of 5,700 years, and its concentration starts to fall as soon as material, animal or vegetable, dies – that is, stops refreshing its carbon from the air or digesting other living tissue. By measuring its concentration, materials can be dated. Famous examples are the Turin Shroud, the Ice Man from 3,300 BC found in the Otztal Alps in 1991, and bottles of fake 'old' whisky.

The most energetic protons from space create showers of sub-atomic particles, most of which decay or are absorbed by the atmosphere. The only radiation that reaches the ground is a flux of muons[18] and this is responsible for the *cosmic* slice in Figure 5. At sea level this delivers about 0.6 millisievert per year in polar latitudes. In equatorial regions the flux is three times smaller because of the shielding effect of the Earth's magnetic field, which sweeps incoming protons away into space. The radiation rises rapidly with height above sea level because of the reduced absorption by the atmosphere.

In the very distant past the flux of radiation was much greater. The Universe itself started from a simultaneous explosion, known as the *Big Bang*, 13.8 billion years ago. The early stages were dominated by particle physics of the kind studied on a small scale at modern research accelerators. After a few minutes the explosion had cooled sufficiently for the distinct nuclei of hydrogen and helium to emerge. But, until 300,000 years later it remained so hot that electrons and nuclei were not bound together. As it cooled further, the heat radiation became non-ionising and atoms of hydrogen and helium appeared for the first time.

Over the next few billion years galaxies and stars formed. These evolved through nuclear fusion in massive stars, creating the heavier atoms that we see around us today, a process called *nucleosynthesis*. Slowly, as the Universe began to settle down, systems of planets formed in the neighbourhood of rotating stars, often composed of lumps of nuclear ash made spherical by gravity. Interplanetary fragments collided with the larger planets and their moons, leaving craters on the surfaces of those without an atmosphere.

---

[18] The muon is an unstable subatomic particle with the properties of a heavy electron, which decays with a half-life of 1.4 microseconds.

This all happened before about 4.5 billion years ago when the Earth was formed and activity became quieter. Ionising radiation still reaches the Earth from hot stars in the form of heat radiation and from exceptional acceleration processes elsewhere in the Universe.

Meanwhile nuclei of the four radioactive series (described in Table 2 on page 42) created during the period of nucleosynthesis continued to decay, although the neptunium series died out long ago. The other three are still going. The abundance of thorium in the Earth's crust is 3 to 10 parts per million by weight. For uranium-238 it is 1.8 to 2.7 parts per million. These values vary depending on the rock formation. There are significant quantities of uranium in sea water because its salts are soluble, unlike those of thorium. Within all natural uranium ores the ratio of uranium-235 to uranium-238 is currently 0.7%. This varies very little as the physical and chemical properties of the two isotopes are almost identical (see page 27) and their relative proportion does not naturally become diluted or enriched except through decay. Highly refined materials may be free of radioactivity but they are exceptional. Wood, concrete, glass and metals are all radioactive to some degree because they contain traces of natural radioisotopes.

A few primordial radioactive nuclei are not members of the four radioactive series. The most abundant is potassium-40 with a half-life of 1.27 billion years. It decays by beta decay, either to calcium-40 or to argon-40, both of which are stable. Potassium is a common element in the Earth's crust (2.1% by weight) and in sea water (0.044%). The regular stable isotope, potassium-39, is the most common and the unstable potassium-40 is only a tiny proportion (0.01117%). Potassium is essential to the electro-chemistry of living cells and forms about 0.15 kg of human body weight. Other radioactive isotopes, such as carbon-14, with shorter lives are found in the environment too, being created afresh by cosmic radiation. Thus carbon-14 and potassium-40 between them account for 7,500 radioactive decays per second in an adult human body. The annual dose from such internal radiation is 0.25 millisievert (see Figure 5).

Two billion years ago the radiation from these nuclei was much as it is today, except that the proportion of uranium-235 in natural uranium was higher. In fact, from the measured half-lives (see Table 2) it is straightforward to calculate that at that time natural uranium contained 3.5% of the faster decaying uranium-235. Today, some nuclear fission reactors use uranium fuel artificially enriched to this proportion, with ordinary water acting as coolant and moderator, in order to maintain a steady nuclear chain reaction. Two billion years ago such enriched fuel and water were available naturally, so that a similar nuclear reactor could occur by itself under the right circumstances. Clear evidence that this actually happened has been found in Gabon, West Africa. This natural nuclear fission reactor, known as the Oklo Reactor [6, 7], ran on its own for up to a million years. In our own time the extraordinary evidence came to light with the discovery that the relative abundance of uranium-235 in this particularly rich uranium deposit lay outside the narrow range found elsewhere in the world. It has been shown that the missing uranium-235 was consumed in the natural reactor cores and that the remains of the resulting fission products are still to be found there. This is significant because this reactor was not decommissioned and buried in a specially selected underground site at great cost. The residue of the uranium fuel and its fission products were left where they lay and have not moved in two billion years. This is an important demonstration of the stability that nuclear waste deposits can have over extremely long periods.

Radiation from radioactive sources in materials such as water, soil or rock reaches the external environment mainly in the form of gamma radiation and radon – alpha and beta radiation are mostly absorbed. Radon is a noble gas with little chemical activity, like helium, neon, argon, krypton and xenon. The isotope radon-222 has a half-life 3.82 days and is formed in the uranium-238 series (Table 3). This radioactive gas, once it has been released into the air, can be inhaled into the lungs where it may be absorbed and decay by alpha emission leaving polonium-218, a non-volatile isotope which decays with a sequence of further alpha emissions. Such alpha radiation has a short range and deposits all its energy in the lungs. On this basis radon would be expected to be a significant source of risk to the health of those who ingest it every day where they live and work. Figure 5 shows radon as a large component of the average human radiation exposure. In fact, it is larger by factors of five or more in certain places, depending on the local geology. A significant question, discussed in Chapter 7, is whether this large variation is reflected in the local incidence of lung cancer.

Chapter 5 Safety and Damage

Poison is in everything, and no thing is without poison. The dosage makes it either a poison or a remedy.

Paracelsus, physician and botanist (1493–1541)

Proportionate effects

We appear to live in a causal world where what happens next is determined by what is happening now. This relationship of cause and effect is easiest to follow if each element of the cause determines its own part of the effect. Such a relation between cause and effect is called linear in mathematical physics. In fact, linearity is really a rather basic and simple idea that does not require fancy mathematics to appreciate.

Here is a simple example. If you are selling me apples and pears, the amount of money that I hand over depends on the number of apples and pears that I buy. Normally, the amount of money that you charge me will simply equal the number of pears times the cost per pear, plus the number of apples times the cost per apple. That is linear – the cost of an extra apple does not depend on the number that I have already bought, or on the number of pears. But it could be otherwise. You could say that extra apples after the first dozen are half price, or that pears are more expensive unless I buy apples too – or that you will pay me to take the first dozen pears, but then charge for further ones. Such pricing is non-linear, and modern supermarkets have certainly learned how to use it to encourage us to buy!

The standard test of linearity is the Superposition Principle. If the total cost is the same as the sum of the cost of buying each apple and pear separately, the pricing is linear. It is true that, if linearity applies, a graph of cost against the number of apples is a straight line – but the reverse is not true. If the slope of the graph for apples changes depending on the number of pears, the pricing is non-linear.

Many aspects of the world described by modern physics are linear or nearly so. Indeed the scientific method is most useful if we can disassemble a problem into pieces and then add the contributions of each back together and still have the right answer.[19] This is the feature that makes telecommunications and audio systems valuable – linearity makes it possible to work backwards and reconstruct the input signals from the output – for example, to hear the strings as separate from the wind instruments when listening to a piece of music. It is linearity that makes it possible to solve problems in quantum mechanics, and that allows light waves and radio-waves to cross through one another without any effect. If what is transmitted on one TV station affected what was received on all the others, that would be non-linear – and not much use either! Similarly, if what we see when we look at one object was influenced to some extent by light from objects that we are not looking at, that would be non-linear too. Fortunately that is not the case for light and electromagnetism. A linear world is like a world of LEGO®, easy to work with scientifically because it is built up of separate bricks.

But not all causes generate effects independently in a linear fashion. Take social behaviour, for instance. The way in which people interact one-to-one gives no information on how they behave as a crowd. So, for example, most aspects of economics are non-linear. Non-linearity occurs in physics too, most obviously in the turbulent flow of fluids.

On page 44 we explained how the relationship between radiation dose and clinical damage has been assumed to be linear – the LNT model. So the question is whether this linear assumption is correct, or not. It will be seen later, that some data fit with the Superposition Principle and some do not, but that linearity is not

---

[19]   Much use is made of approximations and changes of mathematical perspective in the description of modern physics, all with the aim of making problems linear, since then they are far easier to solve and understand.

what we should expect from an understanding of modern biology. The science is about understanding what is occurring at the biological level, not about fitting straight lines to data, or even curves. There was a similar situation in early planetary science. The real reason for discarding Earth-centric cosmology in favour of the Copernican theory was simplicity – the Earth-centric cosmology may have contrived to fit the data, but its calculations lacked simple explanation.

Analysing non-linear systems is possible but not as simple as linear ones. To go back to the apples and pears – if I have accepted your offer of *Buy one get one free* or *One pound off apples when you buy pears*, I may be content with my purchase, but I cannot say how much the apples cost me because the question does not have a simple answer.

Linearity is about independent causes. The superposition test asks two questions. If the response to cause A is α and the response to cause B is β, is the response to $2A$ just 2α; and is the response to A and B together just $\alpha+\beta$? If either of these is untrue, the response is non-linear. We already had an example on page 35 – the response to different volumes of music. It can be dangerous to impress linearity on our view of a problem, just because it makes the assessment easier. A more pragmatic view is suggested by the words of Paracelsus in the early 16th century quoted at the start of the chapter. He understood that the hazard – or benefit – associated with any given action or dosage is often non-linear. Whether administering a drug at a certain dose level is beneficial or harmful is a matter for experimental evidence. In popular parlance we say *you can have too much of a good thing*. Looking at the same situation from the other end, it may be that a little of a bad thing will do no harm, and may even do some good.

Balancing risks

Life presents choices, whether to individuals or to society as a whole. Any choice carries a certain risk and these have to be balanced. Two of these choices involving ionising radiation are illustrated in Figure 6. When a malignant tumour is diagnosed a patient must choose between the likely course of the cancer and a dose of radiotherapy with its radiation side effects (if not a different treatment). Medical advice may guide but there may be mortal dangers either way. Nevertheless, a decision in favour of radiotherapy often results in an extension of enjoyable life, in spite of the high doses that treatment involves. This is a decision for the individual.

(a)

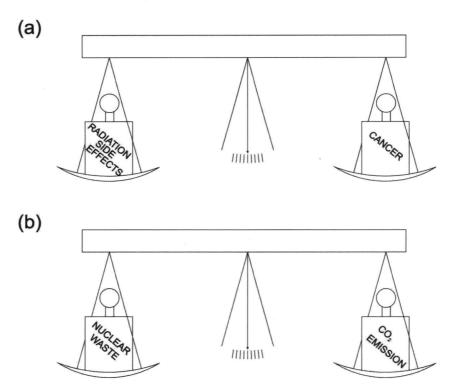

(b)

Figure 6 Choices involving ionising radiation. (a) Balancing risk between the effects of radiotherapy and cancer. (b) Balancing risk between nuclear waste and carbon dioxide emission.

An equally significant choice faces society collectively – whether to minimise the impact of climate change by opting for nuclear power with its attendant waste and perceived radiation risk – or to avoid any effect of radiation while incurring significant greenhouse gas emission. Although the choice is popularly supposed to be equivocal and shrouded by uncertainty, the dangers of ionising radiation are well studied and most of the facts are known. Climate change is a newer problem and there are some aspects to be clarified. But the main elements are understood and decisions have to be made – there is no longer any time to waste. Mankind, the patient, must make the decision.

In classical times the Romans drained swamps and reduced malaria in Italy without knowing the role played by mosquitoes. Similarly, the Victorians who had little understanding of epidemiology built public sewers and fresh water supplies in London. They took firm decisions that controlled the transmission of typhoid, and other diseases, without knowledge of exactly how that control was effected. But we know more about the effects of radioactive contamination and ionising radiation on life than the Victorians did about water-borne diseases.

These are not personal decisions – both climate change and the risks of contamination and radiation exposure affect the population at large. When dangers to others are at stake, it is normal to take a more conservative view of risk than when the hazards are purely personal. But where the choice is between two public global risks, such reticence is misplaced – any degree of precaution should be applied equally to both. Whether a conservative or radical line is taken, the need is to choose the least risky alternative. That is the only question. The answer is not given by appealing for caution in the name of a precautionary principle.

In some countries politicians tentatively support a pro-nuclear power policy; but in others nuclear power is still excluded politically, or even outlawed. Everywhere, leaders and investors need to know whether the public supports decisions in favour of nuclear power. They cannot instruct the court of public opinion – they need the backing of a significant number of people who have read the evidence, questioned it themselves and taken their own view. The following chapters provide evidence to that end.

The comparison to make is that between the combustion of fossil fuel and nuclear fission, as the means of large-scale energy production. Both involve chain reaction processes and so both can be dangerous if not controlled with care. Both produce waste products that need to be managed. But because the chemical energy released in combustion is on a scale some five million times smaller than nuclear energy, the quantity of fuel needed for the same delivered energy is some five million times greater – and so too is the amount of waste generated. In the fossil fuel case, all of the waste is discharged into the atmosphere.[20] In the nuclear case, all of the waste is captured. Since it is largely composed of heavy non-volatile material, it can be safely buried deep in the Earth's crust where it will stay put for many millions of years as in the case of the Oklo Reactor [6, 7]. People have worries about the radiation, the contamination and the cancer, that such waste might cause. In the next two chapters the best world evidence will be used to look carefully at these questions. But first we look more broadly at how we are protected against dangers of all kinds.

Protection of man

At the most basic level man is protected by the provisions of evolutionary biology. These give an extraordinary degree of defence against any agent that interferes at the microscopic level, and human beings are usually quite unaware that this is happening. Many elements of such protection turn out to be general and are not specific to one particular type of threat.

Like other higher animals, man is also protected at a second level by the effect of learned habits and rules, passed down by instruction from one generation to the next. With these we include the laws and regulations to which society assents. This

---

[20] Unless it is captured, a desirable but technically unrealistic task on the scale required.

level of protection is passively learnt and followed, but not necessarily understood.

But, uniquely among creatures, man can also protect himself by fast rational decision-making, based on observation and understanding – that is by judgement, scientific or otherwise. And it is the business of education to hand this faculty of judgement down to later generations. This education is not concerned with learning facts by rote, or with copying from others, but with understanding and the realisation of new solutions.[21] It permits man to adapt to his environment far more rapidly than other animals.

When Charles Darwin published *The Origin of the Species* in 1859 he showed how life on Earth has developed and how species have evolved to cope with the stresses of their environment. The reactions of living organisms to stress are optimised through natural selection – survival is only for those able to protect themselves. The design may not be purposeful, but it is effective nevertheless. However, it is wasteful when there is a change in the pattern of stress – many individuals may perish in the process of selecting the variant that responds in the way best suited to survival. The species may survive, but individuals do not. The selection process may take many generations, and so it is beneficial if generations are short-lived. Otherwise the response would be slower and less effective in the face of stresses that change rapidly.

Today Darwin's ideas are understood to work at the cellular level as well as at the level of whole organisms. Because the turnover through the cell replacement cycle is much faster, an immune reaction to threats at the cellular level can provide rapid protection against disease and infection. But not all threats come at that level.

---

[21] Unfortunately, education is often presented in the media as the ability to recall facts. But the Web is best at that, and education should concentrate on understanding.

Through passive learning, animals teach their progeny how to cope with dangers. The polar bear guides her cubs and plays with them in pretended fights. Mock battles and sibling rivalries between children are rehearsals for later life, when judging the reactions of others becomes all important. Magic and simple deception are essential to children's theatre. Every child in the audience shouts out *He's behind you!* as he sees the villain creeping up behind the actor on the stage. The apprehension and excitement arise from the interplay of fear and knowledge that children feel from an early age. They learn, not to hide from the drama on stage, but to watch and warn or take action, uncomfortable though that may be. Their ability to survive in life will depend on the extent to which they can balance these influences. Much of their play and entertainment is designed to teach them to cope with their imagination of the unseen.

The children's reaction in pantomime highlights that the greatest dangers in life may be the ones that we cannot actually see. In principle, dangers that are seen may be sized up and avoided. Unseen dangers can only be imagined, and, if imagination runs away with itself, confidence and trust collapse and we may end up spooked by things that are actually beneficial. Imagination is a loose cannon – fired without aim, it can destroy that which it seeks to defend. The task is therefore to understand what we cannot see and, at the same time, to control our imagination.

Simple education, with its emphasis on tradition and collective rules that follow the consensus view, does not provide the best guidance, especially when conditions change. The individual with his ability to imagine and think for himself pro-actively is essential. Hans Christian Andersen's tale of *The Emperor's New Clothes* teaches children – and everyone else – the vital lesson, that they should learn to trust the evidence of their own eyes and listen to their own judgement, rather than what they are told. While the vain Emperor with his sycophantic courtiers accepts the majority view that he is wearing a magnificent suit of new clothes, a small boy in the crowd shouts out that he is not wearing any clothes at all. So an important aim of education should be to encourage everyone to challenge accepted opinion.

Man can do better than other creatures. He can use his knowledge and understanding of science to study quite new hazards and work out completely new courses of action, all within a generation – a quicker and less wasteful process than macroscopic evolution. For this, a short generational period is no longer an advantage. A longer lifespan, beginning with an extended period of education is better. It maximises the transmission of wisdom and scientific understanding to younger members of society. For whatever reason, this is the way in which man has been changing in recent centuries, longer lifespan and slower generational turnover. With education, individuals, as well as the species, can respond quickly to a changing environment. Whether mankind as a whole can change his way of life fast enough to respond to climate change remains to be seen.

Damage and stress

Does the chance of damage depend linearly on stress? This is a general question, and it is a good idea to have a look at other instances, before getting to the particular case of the stress that comes from a dose of ionising radiation.

We may think first of a purely mechanical case, like a bridge – how does the survival of a bridge depend on the stresses put upon it? The stresses might come from the traffic crossing it and from the wind and weather buffeting it. If the bridge is designed and maintained properly, when the wind stresses it a little, it will flex a little, but when the wind stops blowing it will spring back to its initial shape so that there is no lasting damage – this is called an elastic response. The temporary flexing is in proportion to the stress, and such a linear mechanical response was first described by Robert Hooke in the 17th century and is known as Hooke's Law.

But that is not the whole story, for if the wind blew very much harder, the bridge might be damaged – that is metal might be permanently twisted, cables snapped or support piers cracked. Then the bridge would not completely recover when the wind ceased and the damage would remain unless repaired. A simple graph can be used to show the damage for a particular stress. Such a curve is called a stress-damage curve or a stress-response curve. In the case of the bridge it might follow a curve like Figure 7b. At low wind strength (stress) there is no permanent movement (damage), as shown by the first flat part, labelled recovery. But for wind strengths above the point labelled threshold, the steeply rising section of curve means that permanent damage increases rapidly until, beyond a certain wind strength, the bridge is destroyed.

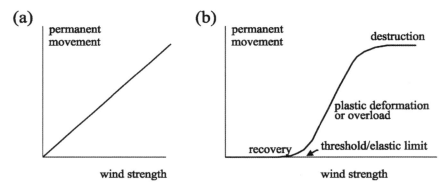

Figure 7   Possible stress-damage curves for a bridge: (a) linear, (b) non-linear.

It is the business of the engineer to design the bridge so that the threshold is high enough that damage will not occur within the range of predicted wind strengths. He may not have complete knowledge of all the information that he needs, in particular about the wind strength to be expected, but he will include a safety factor in his design, perhaps a factor of three or four. However, to allow a large factor would probably not be affordable, and he needs to balance any extra cost against the reduced risk, for in the practical world there is no such sanctuary as absolute safety at finite cost.

Of course, it is possible that the bridge has no spring back and never recovers when deflected. Then the stress-damage curve would follow a straight line similar to Figure 7a (presumably with some limit corresponding to complete failure). Such a dependence of damage on stress is called linear no-threshold behaviour (LNT). But it is a matter of observation that this is not often the case for a bridge, or any other structure. The non-linear S-shape[22] behaviour (Figure 7b) rather than the simple linearity (Figure 7a) is essential to the safety and survival of the bridge.

In other examples the recovery region of the stress-damage curve involves explicit repair – a process that takes a certain time, the repair time. Take the effect of laceration and bruising, for instance. This sort of physical damage to the body usually heals in a few weeks. More serious laceration may leave scar tissue – even if the body apparently recovers its full range of functions, the scar tissue may persist, and in later life become a source of medical complaint. In an extreme case of laceration there may be permanent loss of function, or even death. This stress-damage dependence has similar features to that of the bridge (Figure 7b) – a range with no long-term damage and complete recovery, a range where some long-term damage occurs, and a range where permanent loss of function ensues.

Time to repair

Repair takes a certain time and any further stress, incurred before the repair is completed, adds to the risk of passing the threshold of permanent damage. Conversely, any biological damage described by LNT would suggest an absence of any repair mechanism – and a failure of biological development to evolve such protection. In biology this is very unlikely and, unless both data and evolutionary circumstances unambiguously indicate otherwise, it is unreasonable to assume that LNT applies.

---

[22] This shape is sometimes described as *sigmoid*, rather than S-shaped.

For a non-linear response the important questions are: Is the shape of the curve as sketched in Figure 7b, as expected through repair or feedback?[23] How long is the repair time? And what is the threshold for lasting damage? For the bridge, the repair might be the effect of an explicit maintenance schedule. A bridge that is inspected and repaired regularly is liable to suffer permanently, only if the integrated effect of damage between inspections exceeds a threshold. Repair would make good any damage – re-mortar the bricks, replace bent struts and protect from the elements with a new coat of paint, before the next major storm. Such a bridge will continue in service for a long time if the maintenance schedule is of adequate frequency. This is the way in which machinery and structures are usually kept serviceable and safe. The bridge only suffers permanent damage, if the stresses within a maintenance period accumulate elements of minor unrepaired damage, that together exceed the critical threshold.

There is no fancy technology here – just old-fashioned common sense. But when looked at in the right way, this is often true. From a safety point of view the design of the bridge and its maintenance procedure form a single system, characterised by a repair time and a net damage threshold. Stresses accumulated within the repair time contribute to passing the threshold of permanent damage; but stresses separated by longer periods do not accumulate because repair is effected in between.

Collective dose

Suppose that a group of people is subjected to a stress of a kind to which LNT does apply. If K is the slope of the line in Figure 7a, then the damage to each individual would be K times stress suffered by each. By addition, the total damage suffered by the group would be directly determined by the sum of their individual stresses with the same slope K. Since what is of

---

[23] It is sometimes supposed that, if it is not linear, it should be assumed to be quadratic, or linear + quadratic, instead. There is no reason for such an assumption.

interest is the combined risk to the group, it would be simplest just to measure the sum of stresses – this is called the collective dose. The damage is then found by multiplying this by K. This mathematical result is particularly simple, and it is rather neat and easy to work with. From a regulatory position all that is needed is to add up the total collective dose and multiply by K – and there you have the collective damage, or risk assessment.

In particular, for radiation the collective dose can be calculated in this way – simply add each equivalent dose measured in sievert for all those individuals involved. This prescription is set out by the International Atomic Energy Agency (IAEA) [8 p.24] to be a self-evident basic method:

> *The total impact of the radiation exposure due to a given practice or source depends on the number of individuals exposed and on the doses they receive. The collective dose, defined as the summation of the products of the mean dose in the various groups of exposed people and the number of individuals in each group, may <u>therefore</u> be used to characterize the radiation impact of a practice or source. The unit of collective dose is the man-sievert (man-Sv).* [underlined emphasis added]

[*Note added in proof*: It may be significant that this webpage was removed from the IAEA website at some time between 10 February and 17 April 2009. Perhaps the IAEA no longer consider it self-evident, or true.]

But is the total damage (or detriment) related to the collective dose determined in this way? The conclusion drawn in the second sentence quoted above does not follow if the reaction of living tissue to radiation is not linear. Then the use of the collective dose would not be applicable – and its use would give quite wrong answers. In the next chapter we shall see whether this is the case, but first, we look at some other general examples, some for which collective dose is relevant and others for which it is not.

A goldsmith might be concerned at the financial loss due to filings and polishings of metal that get thrown out when they are swept up with the dust on his shop floor. He assesses the metal lost, big and small, adds it up (the collective dose) and multiplies by the price of gold (K), and he has a good figure for the related financial loss. In this example LNT applies, for there is no regeneration mechanism for the lost gold.

However, the use of collective dose gives the wrong answer if there is a repair process making LNT inapplicable. Then the compilation of a collective dose would be dangerous in the sense that it would encourage a total risk assessment that is significantly in error. How about the risk incurred by humans through blood loss? Like gold, blood is highly valued. Since the body of any adult contains about 5 litres of blood, a loss of this much at one time by one person would be fatal. If a group of people suffer blood loss in an accident, it is true that the more people there are in the group, and the more blood that each loses, the more serious would be the accident. It is tempting to quantify this by adding up the total blood loss, the collective dose (in man-litres). If LNT applied, the gravity of an incident would be determined by this collective dose. Since the loss of 5 litres by an individual is fatal, the effective number of fatalities arising from the incident would simply be the volume of lost blood in litres divided by 5, the number of man-litres corresponding to one death. If that were true, then every 10 donors visiting a blood clinic to donate half a litre of blood would incur one fatality!

Why does the use of collective dose with an LNT assessment give a nonsense answer in this case? The crucial point is that over a period of time a healthy individual makes good any loss of blood – so the loss is repaired. The use of the collective dose ignores this. Each adult can lose half a litre of blood and it will be replaced within a few weeks, with no risk whatsoever. So the loss of 100 litres of blood by 200 people happens in a successful blood donor clinic. The loss of 100 litres by 50 people over a year gives no ill effects either, although lost by 20 people over a short period might cause fatalities. We see that an assessment of risk using collective dose can lead to absurd conclusions, if there is repair and, therefore, non-linearity. And the erroneous analysis is not corrected by fiddling with mathematics, such as using a quadratic dependence on collective dose. The repair mechanism simply invalidates the use of the collective dose.

Doses (or stresses) may be either acute or chronic. If the response to a single acute dose is known and the repair time is known, a reasonable assessment of the effect of a regularly repeated or chronic dose can be made. In the case of blood donation this was assumed above – a donation of half a litre every few months creates no hazard. However, any extra blood donations within one repair time would have a cumulative effect. Generally, this means that, if the threshold of damage due to a single acute dose is A, then the threshold of damage due to a chronic or repeated dose rate is A/T, where T is the repair time. The shorter the repair time, the higher is the threshold for damage due to a chronic dose rate. Reality may be a little more complicated – there may be more than one repair process and more than one time.

Safety margins

The safety margin incorporated in the design of an affordable structure like a bridge might be a factor of four, say, and it seems that nature also employs modest margins. For example, in the case of blood loss by an individual, the margin is 10 between the safe stress of a half litre loss and the fatal stress of a 5 litre loss.

Another example is the risk caused by fluctuations in body temperature. These are normally stabilised by balancing metabolic activity with the cooling effects of blood circulation and perspiration. Variations associated with intense exercise or a light fever amount to a degree or so and cause no lasting damage. But changes of two degrees or more in tissue temperature are potentially serious, and after a high fever a period of rest is often prescribed. At the other extreme, a temperature excursion of 20 degrees or more can cause cells to melt and cease to function. Leaving aside the details, a variety of feedback mechanisms is seen to stabilise temperature, again with a safety factor of a few between the onset of damage and a fatal condition.

None of these factors is precisely defined, of course, but they fall in the same range. The point is that the use of a much higher safety margin would be wasteful of resources, in biology as in the engineering of a bridge. Nature is a master at balancing risks against resource costs, and mankind would do well to study her example. So what safety margin is affordable in connection with ionising radiation? We shall consider the uestion in later chapters.

Multiple causes

It is common experience that a patient, whose health is poor on account of one stress, is likely to be adversely affected by a second imposed at the same time – more likely anyway than by the two stresses acting separately at different times. If the response were linear this would not be the case – the effect of the stresses would simply add. Indeed, the collective prognosis would be the same, even if the stresses were experienced by different people! But this is not so because the response is non-linear. In the language of the analogy of the apples and pears, the price of an apple is different if you have bought a pear.

It has been found that the combined mortality due to malaria and AIDS exceeds the sum of each separately [9]. This is a failure of linearity and has important implications for world health. Malaria and AIDS are unrelated, but they both load the immune system, which has some threshold for failure. But we do not need to understand the mechanism to appreciate this. This is simply the effect of non-linearity. The mortality due to AIDS and due to malaria cannot be unscrambled, just as the pricing of apples and pears could not be unscrambled when the pricing was non-linear.

In normal health care, following an incident of excessive stress, the treatment of a patient usually calls for a period of convalescence, completely removed from sources of further stress. Typically the duration of such recuperation is about a week or so in simple cases. As a result of this period of inactivity, risk of long-term damage is minimised, and later the usual pattern of stress may be re-imposed with full functionality.

So here is a measure of a typical clinical repair time. This is familiar common sense, not new science. But it is not compatible with LNT.

With advancing age the threshold of damage for most stresses becomes lower, whether from the accumulated effect of scar tissue or from a general loss of protective immunity. The rapid repair processes due to cell replacement and the quick convalescence of youth become slower.

Beneficial and adaptive effects

To speak of stress suggests that the response is always negative. This may not be the case, as Paracelsus remarked. A dose of a drug may have a beneficial effect or a harmful one, depending on the dose.

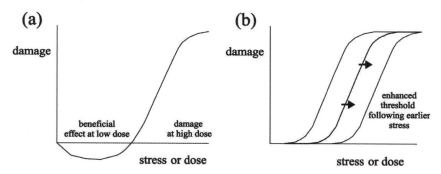

Figure 8 **Sketches of the dependence of damage on dose, (a) where a low dose is beneficial, and (b) where the response is adaptive with the threshold increased by a history of previous doses.**

The effect of the drug paracetamol provides a trivial but familiar example. One hundred tablets taken at once by a single individual would be fatal. Spread evenly among fifty patients, they would not be the cause of any death, but might have a positive impact on health. Such non-linearity is a normal feature of toxicology. For instance the dose-damage curve might be as sketched in Figure 8a. Over a certain range of dose the damage is negative, that is to say the drug is beneficial. But for a greater dose it may be harmful, or even fatal.

The process of evolution does not simply determine an unchanging stress-damage response curve. It also provides an ability to track the pattern of past stresses so that the response curve itself changes. For example, the dose-response relationship may depend on the pattern of earlier stresses, as suggested by the qualitative sketch, Figure 8b. The administration of low doses may develop an ability to tolerate higher doses. Such a pattern was first seen in the extraordinary discovery by Edward Jenner in 1796 that giving a mild dose of disease (cowpox) to a patient provides greatly enhanced protection against a more virulent strain (smallpox). The study of this effect is the science of immunology. It can provide fast adaption for the individual by selection dynamics at the cellular level. In such cases the individual is quite unaware that he is receiving this protection.

But there is a further kind of rapid adaption that is not at the cellular level and is conscious. This may be illustrated by returning to the example of the bridge. What happens when a bridge fails? In a non-cognitive world engineers might simply select, without thinking, a design of replacement bridge by copying one of those that happened to remain standing at the time. The response time, the time for bridges to be re-designed for a changing environment, would be long and characterised by the natural life of a bridge. But that is not what happens in the modern world of man. Following the failure of a bridge an enquiry is held. The reaction to the collapse of the Interstate-35 bridge in Minneapolis on 1 August 2007 provides an apt example. Within 24 hours all aspects of the design that failed were under consideration [10]. Design modifications were put in hand, maintenance and inspection procedures reconsidered, models built and tested, and all lessons learnt applied to other bridges of similar design. This is a proactive cognitive process made possible by intelligence. Then the survival prospects for all such bridges benefit from the fast adaptive response.

Many creatures engage in some kind of education, for only those species that pass on beneficial habits to their young enjoy enhanced survival characteristics. But such education by tradition and rote is slow to change, and a short life and generation gap are necessary to speed the reaction to change. Rapid cognitive adaption based on understanding is quite different – it needs a much longer and intensive period of education, and so is best suited to a long lifespan with slow generational turnover. It characterises a proper university education where students are taught to think for themselves, rather than simply to regurgitate facts and formulae as they may have been taught at school.

Adaptive behaviour reduces risks, and examples may be found in quite diverse organisational structures. For example, during the troubles in Northern Ireland in the 1970s and 1980s there were many hospital casualties requiring serious plastic surgery, and the surgical teams there developed exceptional skills. Consequently, anyone else needing plastic surgery at the time was well advised to go to Northern Ireland for treatment. Of course, this just underlines the efficacy of genuine training for any demanding activity. Children need to practise crossing the road. Drivers need to learn how to coordinate the ability to think with the timing and judgement required when driving a car. Practice and experience of the stress involved are necessary for safety, but the essential step in such training is thinking.

Humans have this superior ability to survive. The new danger of climate change is a pressing problem in response to which we need to adapt our way of life. This involves reaching a balanced assessment of all related dangers and keeping a sharp lookout for any sign that our current assessment of any such danger may have been misjudged, for instance the effect of radiation on life.

Surprise at Chernobyl

On 26 April 1986 reactor number four at the Chernobyl nuclear power station in the Ukraine exploded. How this happened is now well understood, as described in the international reports by the Organisation for Economic Cooperation and Development (OECD/NEA) [11], the International Atomic Energy Authority (IAEA) [12] and the World Health Organisation (WHO) [13]. The Russian-built reactor had poor stability and lacked any kind of safety containment vessel. It was in the control of an inexperienced team who did not understand the consequences of the dangerous tests that they decided to undertake. The resulting power surge caused an excess pressure of superheated steam within the water-cooled reactor which blew the top off the structure. Further chemical explosions and fire followed the exposure of the reactor core to the environment. Because of the excessively high temperature some of the core material rose into the upper atmosphere where it was transported over long distances. This included all of the volatile radioactive iodine and much of the lighter fission products. The less volatile heavy elements, such as uranium and plutonium, remained within the reactor or were scattered within shorter distances.

The accident was made worse by the failure of the Soviet administration to cope with the situation as it developed. It tried to hide the news on the international front. Locally it failed immediately to provide iodine tablets and give out the public information required. Later it over-reacted, forcibly relocating 116,000 of the local population without warning, so causing panic and social dislocation. It is probable that this caused more damage to life than the radiation itself. The incident can be seen as one of the elements that lead to the socio-economic collapse of the whole Soviet Empire.

Meanwhile at Chernobyl, an exclusion zone was established around the site. International programmes were undertaken in an attempt to bury radioactive material to keep it out of the natural food chain and major water courses. After the evacuation only those employed in the clean-up programme were supposed to enter the exclusion zone, and the authorities strove to attract further international funds to spend on the reactor and surrounding site. This worldwide attention secured some welcome resources for a depressed region – it was not in anyone's interest there to make less of the accident and its consequences. It followed the story of the failure of the reactor at Three Mile Island[24] in 1979 and the world press accepted the Chernobyl story as confirming a general distrust of nuclear safety. Early international reports sought to record the facts about the radiation and the spread of contamination, but did not attempt to question the overall risks to human health. In this way security and resources were maximised for a situation in which panic and social dislocation were manifest.

But in recent years those who have visited the site have reported surprise. Instead of the wasteland they had expected, they found that wildlife is surviving, and in some cases thriving, in spite of the radiation levels. An American reporter, Mary Mycio [14], originally from Ukraine, has spent much time there and written eloquently of the flora and fauna that she found. A BBC documentary [15] on Chernobyl was shown in July 2006 with similar conclusions. An excerpt recorded:

> *Yesterday we spoke to an expert on the wildlife of the Chernobyl zone, who surprised us by saying that animals did not seem to be too bothered by the present level of radiation. He said he had searched for rodents in the sarcophagus, and had not found any – but he put this down to the absence of food rather than the presence of the reactor's highly radioactive remains. Birds nested inside the sarcophagus, he said, and did not appear to suffer any adverse effects.*

These observations raise a simple question, is there something wrong with the accepted orthodox view of the dangers of radiation to life? Evidently the animals, birds and plants in their habitat at Chernobyl are radioactive, as anticipated. Yet, in some cases at least, they are no worse off now with the radioactivity but without human settlements than they were previously with

---

[24] In the Three Mile Island accident control of the reactor was lost but the containment vessel was not ruptured, there was no loss of life and the release of radioactivity was small.

human habitation but no radiation. Is it true that human habitation is as bad for the environment as a large dose of nuclear contamination? We should question anew many of the old assumptions used in the analysis of the effects of radiation on life. In particular, have we allowed the use of LNT to give unreasonable safety assessments, as would be the case if we were to apply it to the dangers of blood loss? Having opened the question with these non-scientific observations, we should examine the data and the science.

Chapter 6 A Single Dose of Radiation

What happens to molecules

Radiation comes, either as a stream of energetic charged particles, or as a flux of electromagnetic radiation, that is neutral photons.[25] But radiation cannot have any effect on materials, including living tissue, unless some of its energy is absorbed. This absorbed energy is not spread out uniformly through the irradiated region, but occurs as a series of collisions or events, as they are called. If the absorbed energy is high, the number of events is increased but the character of each event remains the same. In a typical event an individual atom or molecule receives enough energy to be broken up, occasionally sending off a secondary charged electron or photon, perhaps with enough energy to cause a few further events on its own account.

In a beam of charged particle radiation each incident charge generates its own string of independent events called a track. Along a track events are separated by a fraction of a micron – the density of events depends on the speed and magnitude of the charge, and also on the density of the material, but not much on its composition. As it makes its track the charge may be scattered sideways a little as a result of the events, as well as gradually losing energy with each successive event. The more energetic it is initially, the further it goes, until finally it stops at the end of its range. The rate at which it loses energy along its track is called its *linear energy transfer* (LET) – this is simply a matter of the density of events.

Photons on the other hand do not create long tracks but give isolated events, more thinly spread out, often with emission of an energetic electron or secondary photon. As a result photons in a beam have an exponential distribution of penetration described by an average range, quite unlike the rather sharply defined

---

[25] Leaving aside neutron radiation, which is less common in the environment.

length distribution of charged particle tracks. This average range is strongly dependent on the material composition – in fact on the atomic number Z of its atoms. In particular, for high Z atoms like lead, the absorption is high and the range short. It is not just that there are more electrons in a high Z atom, each electron is more tightly bound and the effect per electron is greater. This is why lead is used to shield X-rays in places where radiation is used, including medical and dental facilities.

These collisions or events involve either an atom as a whole or a single electron in an atom – the nuclei of the material play almost no part and are unaffected. Generally the impact of ionising radiation on material is rather indiscriminate. This may be explained in terms of an energy hierarchy:

1/40 eV		1/10 eV		10–100 eV		1,000,000 eV
random	<<	biological	<<	collision	<<	incident
thermal		activation		event		radiation
energy	.	energy		energy		energy

The energy absorbed in a collision or event is in the range of a few electron volts[26], say 10–100 eV. Such energies are very small compared with the energy of the incident radiation, but much larger than the delicate activation energies of the biological molecules essential to life, which are on the scale of 1/10 eV. These in turn are robust compared with the random thermal energies with which molecules hit one another, simply because they are warm, 1/40 eV. This hierarchy means that the energy dumped in an event is too small to disrupt any nucleus but any molecule hit in an event suffers major damage – there is no fine tuning. Different types of ionising radiation affect the spatial distance between events, but often have less influence on the energy of each event. Equally, any kind of molecule may be hit and become the site of an event. This is the sense in which the damage caused by radiation exposure is indiscriminate.

---

[26] This does not include the energy given to a secondary electron, if any.

In the immediate aftermath of the passage of the radiation, distinct destruction sites of molecular debris are left where the events occurred. Very quickly the highly reactive pieces of broken molecules, called hot chemical radicals, disrupt other molecules that may have been undamaged in the initial event. This is the chemical stage of the story in which radiation and radioactivity play no part. In organic matter the presence of oxygen can prolong the destructive activity of these radicals, and so too can water molecules (H_2O) through the production of OH radicals. Anti-oxidants are biological molecules that have the opposite effect by mopping up and neutralising radicals. But, this rampage soon stops leaving relatively quiescent chemical debris.

What happens to cells

If the material is living tissue, any molecule affected by an event may have lost its ability to fulfil its biological function in a cell. Much the same kind of damage can be caused by agents other than ionising radiation – for example, by an exceptional random collision with another molecule, or by chemical action, in particular oxidation. What may be different about the effect of ionising radiation is the number of such damaged molecules within a small region. But the next stage of the story is biological in any case, whether the initial cause was radiation or chemical attack.

Living tissue is composed of cells, the units of life. These cells have a large range of size, shape and structure according to their function. However, in each case there is a cell skin that encloses both the active proteins and the genetic records that are encoded in DNA. These records, held in the nucleus of the cell, determine the production of the cell's proteins, and thence its function and reproductive cycle. The complete DNA record in a cell also contains the information for all of the other cells.

If a protein molecule is damaged and ceases to function, its role is usually taken over by others that remain intact. Such damaged molecules are then naturally replaced along with the undamaged ones in the next cycle of cell regeneration without harmful effect.

The only way that errors (whether caused by radiation or chemical attack) can get copied to later generations of cells is through damage to the DNA record. If the DNA is altered, its copies in subsequent generations of cells may be altered too. However, that is too simplistic as it turns out, for there are several ways in which such errors in the DNA get progressively weeded out.

Evidence at high dose

Before following this biological story further, we look at some actual evidence that shows the effect of radiation on animals and humans. Do they show a dose-damage curve similar to the ones for other stresses that we looked at? Does the curve have the characteristic sigmoid shape (Figure 7b) suggesting some kind of protective repair mechanism? Or is it described by the straight line of the LNT hypothesis (Figure 7a)?

Figure 9 shows data on mortality due to acute doses of radiation with different intensities. Data on laboratory rats given a single exposure of X-rays to the whole body are sketched in Figure 9a. The curve follows the familiar non-linear S-shape that we have come to expect. A dose of about 7,000 millisievert is sufficient to cause the death of 50% of rats, but with half that dose less than 1% die. If LNT were correct, the curve would be replaced by the heavy dashed line and 25% of the rats would be expected to die from this halved dose. The experiment can be repeated with many rats so that uncertainties are small. Evidently the response is non-linear, at these high doses at least.

But how different are humans from rats? At the Chernobyl accident there were 237 workers who were exposed to intense radiation in the early stages of fighting the fire. Of these, 28 died of acute radiation sickness in the following few weeks. The mortality of these workers is shown in four bands of radiation dose by the crosses in Figure 9b. The width of each cross indicates the range of dose for that band; the vertical height represents the statistical uncertainty in the measured mortality

(a)

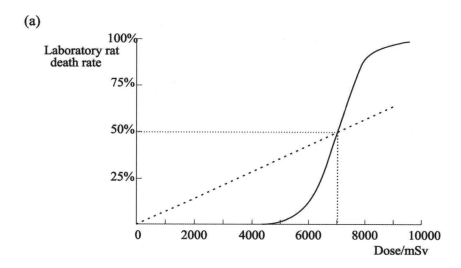

(b)

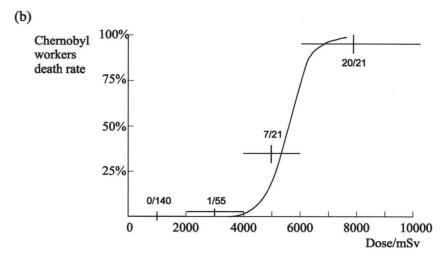

Figure 9   (a) The observed mortality of laboratory rats for different radiation doses (solid curve) compared with LNT (dashed line). The vertical and horizontal dotted lines are solely to guide the eye. (After Henriksen and Maillie [16].) (b) The mortality of Chernobyl workers (crosses) in four dose bands compared with the mortality of the rats, as in (a) but scaled to a slightly lower dose.

given the small number of workers.[27] So in the highest band 20 out of 21 died, in the next band 7 out of 21, in the third band 1 out of 55, and in the lowest band out of 140 all survived. Also shown is the S-shaped curve found for the rats, scaled to give 50% human mortality at 5,500 millisievert instead of 7,000 millisievert.

The Chernobyl data and this curve match well, given the uncertainty reflected in the size of the crosses. Of course the human experiment may not be repeated accurately with many subjects like the rat experiment. Even so, the conclusion is clearly that the dose-mortality curve for humans at high doses is not described by LNT but follows a typical non-linear S shape.

Repair mechanisms

The discussion in Chapter 5 would suggest that this non-linearity arises from one or more repair mechanisms. Discovering these has been a matter for biological study with cells in the laboratory and with further experiments on animals. We start by thinking about what kind of protection biology might have developed.

Imagine a similar situation in a non-scientific context – a business liable to random attack from fire or robbery. Good management would implement some defensive procedures. The first of these could be to equip all areas with fire extinguishers and an alarm system that is activated by any intruder or fire outbreak. Next multiple copies of all working documents should be made so that, if one copy is lost or damaged, others would survive. Then a rapid reaction unit capable of quickly repairing simple damage to master records. Another line would be a continuous programmed replacement of all elements of the structure. Finally a regime of cleanliness to remove all unwanted material as quickly as possible. Interestingly, it seems that cellular biology has developed elements of defence along similar lines.

---

[27] These are standard statistical errors so that the probability that the true result falls within the range shown is 63%.

The equivalent of the fire extinguishers is the promotion of anti-oxidant molecules in cells, capable of quenching the radicals produced by radiation at the early or chemical stage of radiation damage. These can cope also with the early effects of any oxidative attack, so no special provision is needed for radiation. The alarm system is provided by inter-cellular signalling such that cells cooperate and warn other cells whenever an attack is detected. Protection by copying takes place at two levels. Within each cell there are multiple copies of many functional proteins. The effectiveness of this is shown by the observation that, in the early stages of a cell's life cycle when the number of copies is smallest, its sensitivity to radiation is greatest. But there are no spare copies in each cell of the DNA with its genetic information. However, the cells themselves are copied and the DNA in each cell contains the complete record for the whole organism, not just its own part. Each cell contains enzymes that repair single breaks in DNA strands – these enzymes are the rapid reaction unit in our analogy. Because DNA has the special double strand helix, a molecule that suffers a single strand break (SSB) remains connected and can be mended without error. Test tube experiments show that these enzymes can repair most single breaks within a few hours. Double strand breaks (DSBs) are less frequent. When they occur they can still be repaired but may be mis-repaired. A further level of protection is needed to cope with these.

Copies of whole cells are produced dynamically by the process of cell division and programmed replacement. While functioning cells divide to create new ones, existing cells are regularly scrapped. Cells may die of their own accord, they may be encouraged to die by inter-cellular signalling or they may be attacked. Anyway these mechanisms provide discrimination in favour of cells recognised as native over those that have changed or are foreign. This organised cleansing process is called apoptosis. The disposal of dead cells and other debris is undertaken by cells called macrophages.

So there are levels of protection within a cell, and should they fail there are active renewal mechanisms to replace whole cells. The details are not important in this brief sketch – the point is that these mechanisms exist and are effective. They were not developed specifically to cope with the detritus left by a dose of ionising radiation – they are mostly employed to cope with chemical attack and random breakages. They are active on various timescales from hours to a few weeks, depending on the particular organ and the age of the individual. Important to the working of these defence mechanisms is the fact that cells communicate – the inter-cell signalling. The word gets around that this cell has been damaged or that another needs to be scrapped. The immunological process then sees to it that such cells do not survive.

This type of behaviour by cells is not unlike the way in which people behave in crowds. Social groups that survive do so by selection and by robust rejection of those that do not belong. Often this is not a pleasant process and includes all manner of discrimination – it can even become self-destructive with witch hunts and other types of social self-harm.

The scientific study of this sociology of cells and its response to ionising radiation is the subject of radiobiology. This is studied in the laboratory with cells in solution, and also in experiments with laboratory animals similar to man, such as rats and mice. We shall focus on what can be learnt from human data, because it is slightly easier to follow and also because that is what we are really concerned about. We will see how the data confirm the picture that the radiobiologists find in their laboratory work.

According to this picture the repair and protection mechanisms that cope well with low doses are overwhelmed at higher doses, and this naturally gives rise to the sigmoid curve. Following a high dose, cell division is suspended or delayed and more cells die than are created. Some organs in the body have a particularly rapid turnover of cell population under normal circumstances – for example, the digestive tract. As a result these are the first to fail following a very high acute dose. The symptoms of acute radiation sickness are vomiting, diarrhoea, dehydration and death in a few days, or weeks at the outside. This was the experience of those who died from a high dose at Chernobyl (Figure 9b). Cancer is not involved in these cases.

These observations are for high doses. How effective are these repair mechanisms for lower acute doses? Then the repair and cell replacement mechanisms operate, but an occasional DNA error survives.

Low and intermediate doses

The effect of lesser doses of ionising radiation may be an increase in the observed incidence of various cancers that become evident long after the exposure. These cancers vary in mortality. The cause in an individual case cannot be determined, but statistically, incidence can often be related to smoking, diet or radiation – or be apparently without cause, that is spontaneous. In all cases the origin is understood as a chemical attack of some kind on the DNA. Even when a significant radiation exposure has been experienced, the cancer rate due to other causes is still much larger (with the exception of thyroid cancer). The contribution of ionising radiation may then be impossible to measure with any confidence unless data are available for very large populations in receipt of significant doses of radiation.

Let us take a fictitious example to illustrate the point. Suppose that there are two groups, each of 10,000 people. In the first group the chance of dying of cancer in 50 years is 10%, but in the second it is 10.5% because this group has received a certain dose of radiation. If the test were repeated many times the average number of cancer deaths in the two groups would be 1,000 and 1,050. However, if data are available for only one such test, the number in the first group would fluctuate statistically, being greater than 1,030 for 18% of such tests and greater than 1,060 for 2.5% of them.[28] Similarly the number of deaths

---

[28] These variations are reliable statistical results, independent of this problem.

counted in the second group would be less than 1,020 for 18% of tests and less than 990 in 25% of tests. So comparing the number of deaths in one such test would be quite inconclusive, simply because of the statistical uncertainty. If the number of people in each group was 10 times larger or the radiation dose (or its effect) was much greater, the test might provide meaningful evidence. Then to reach a firm conclusion the radiation dose for each group member must be measured and checks applied to ensure that other causes of cancer are not confusing the situation – these are called confounding effects.

There are relatively few such sources of data and these have received a great deal of attention from researchers. The basic data have been discussed between laboratories from all over the world and the results may be found on the Web. The largest source is the medical records of the human survivors of Hiroshima and Nagasaki. Then there is the Chernobyl accident, and we have looked at the high dose data from there already. Another large source of internationally compiled data is concerned with the incidence of lung cancer and its correlation with the radiation environment in which people live. There are the health records of those who have worked with radioactive material over the decades, including medical radiologists. Then there are the people who painted the dials of watches and other instruments with luminous paint in the decades up to 1950. They absorbed quantities of radium that remained with them as an internal source of alpha radiation. Finally there are data for patients who have received radiation in the course of medical diagnostic imaging, or, more significantly, in radiotherapy treatment. We look at these in this chapter and the next.

Survivors of Hiroshima and Nagasaki

The data that have been studied most are the health records of the survivors of Hiroshima and Nagasaki – the number of individuals is large, they have been studied for over 50 years, and the individual doses cover a wide range with an average 160 millisievert, a significant intermediate exposure.

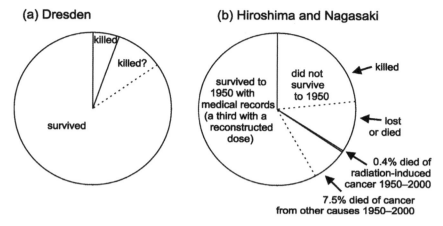

Figure 10 Pie charts of the mortality of the bombings of (a) Dresden and (b) Hiroshima and Nagasaki. The numbers killed immediately are not well known but the history of those who survived to 1950 is well documented.

At the time of the bombing the population of the cities was 429,000. It has been estimated that in the explosion, the fire and the early effects of radiation more than 103,000 died. Naturally, early information is lacking but the data become more reliable from 1950 after which the medical records of 283,000 individual survivors have been followed. This leaves 43,000, either dead, unaccounted for or lost in the period between 1945 and 1950. Figure 10b shows the situation graphically. At Hiroshima and Nagasaki the chance of not surviving until 1950 was about a third. This is compared with about 10% or more at Dresden, Figure 10a. How many inhabitants of the Japanese cities in 1945 succumbed to radiation-induced cancer in the period 1950–2000? Such a question could not be answered in earlier decades and therefore an extremely cautious view was taken. Today, no such provisional caution needs to be applied, because the question can be answered. The detailed numbers are given below but may be summarised. The chance of surviving to 1950 and then dying of cancer between 1950 and 2000 was 7.9%. As will be seen later, the chance of surviving and then dying of radiation-induced cancer during this period was only 0.4%. This is much less than might have been expected, and so we should look in some detail at how it is derived.

Of course no resident of these cities was wearing a radiation monitor on the day the bombs were dropped, but it has been possible to estimate the individual radiation exposure for 86,955 of the survivors.[29] This has been done in three different ways, allowing cross checks to be made.

The first estimate comes from a knowledge of exactly where the individual was relative to the centre of the detonation and calculating the radiation flux received, taking into account the absorption of intervening material. The second method uses the incidence of chromosome damage, which retains a long memory of radiation dose. This method, called FISH (fluorescence in situ hybridisation), is found to be non-linear, itself showing a failure of LNT [17]. The third comes from measuring the radiation damage recorded in the teeth and bones of each survivor using electron spin resonance (ESR) [18]. This determines the density of unpaired electrons – in such solids these remain a frozen record of ionising radiation exposure even after several years. Individual doses have been re-analysed using these methods on more than one occasion, most recently in 2002.

The subsequent medical records of the survivors with reconstructed dose have been compared with those of a control group of 25,580 people who lived in Japan outside the bombed cities and received no radiation. Data on the mortality from leukaemia and solid cancers have been compiled for both sets. Data on other causes of death, and also the effect on pregnancies and other sensitive conditions, have been compiled, but here we concentrate on the cancers. The reason for this choice is that a statistically significant radiation-induced effect is seen for these

---

[29] The proportion of post-1950 radiation-induced cancer deaths is assumed to be the same for all the survivors as that for those with a reconstructed dose. The figures are 0.5% and 0.1% for solid cancers and leukaemia, and these are then multiplied by 0.6, the probability of survival to 1950.

cancers, whereas the increase in the incidence of other conditions is reported to be smaller and less certain.[30]

Radiation-induced cancers

Table 4 Data from Preston et al [19 Table 7] on the number of deaths from leukaemia between 1950 and 2000 among the survivors of Hiroshima and Nagasaki with measured doses, compared with the number expected using data for the inhabitants of nearby cities.

Dose range millisievert	Number of survivors	Survivor deaths actual	Survivor deaths expected	Extra risk per 1000
<5	37,407	92	84.9	−0.1 to 0.5
5 to 100	30,387	69	72.1	−0.4 to 0.2
100 to 200	5,841	14	14.5	−0.7 to 0.6
200 to 500	6,304	27	15.6	1.0 to 2.6
500 to 1,000	3,963	20	9.5	3.8 to 6.6
1,000 to 2,000	1,972	39	4.9	14 to 20
>2,000	737	25	1.6	25 to 39
All	86,955	296	203	0.9 to 1.3

[30] Shimizu et al [20] have shown that there have been between 140 and 280 deaths (up to 1990) from other diseases that are statistically related to radiation. They report no evidence for any radiation effect below 500 milli-sievert.

Table 4 shows the data for leukaemia deaths among survivors with reconstructed dose. Each row describes a band or range of radiation dose, and in each case the mortality is compared with what would be expected using the death rate among the control sample. In total 296 survivors died of leukaemia in the 50-year period while only 203 would be expected in the absence of radiation. So approximately 93 extra deaths in the population of 86,955 are attributable statistically to radiation-induced leukaemia, although of course it is not possible to say which ones were spontaneous and which radiation-induced. The data in each dose band are summarised in the final column, which shows the number of extra deaths in 50 years per 1,000 people – this is given as a range described by the statistical error.[31] To put such numbers in perspective, if the chance of dying of radiation-induced leukaemia in 50 years is 1 in 1,000, then average life expectancy is reduced by 2 weeks. The data in the rows of the table for any dose less than 200 millisievert are consistent with no risk, and also with a reduction in life expectancy of less than 2 weeks. For the 15% of the survivors who received more than 200 millisievert, a definite risk is measured. Above 1,000 millisievert (3% of the survivors) the risk is greater than 21 per 1,000, a reduction in life expectancy of about a year. In summary, out of the 296 survivors who died of leukaemia over 50 years, some 203 would have died in this way in the absence of radiation. And the incidence of radiation-induced leukaemia is smaller than the incidence of natural leukaemia, even when those who received higher doses are included.

Table 5 shows similar data to Table 4 but for survivor deaths due to cancers other than leukaemia. The total number of these fatalities was 10,127, much greater than for leukaemia. The majority occurred naturally or were related to diet or smoking. This background count is shown as 9,647, the number of expected deaths, based on the control sample. The difference, 480 deaths, is the number probably caused by the radiation. This

---

[31] The measured risk in parts per 1,000 is given with a one standard deviation range. This means that the actual risk has a chance of 2-to-1 of being within the quoted range.

is half of 1% of the survivors and 5% of those who died of cancer unrelated to radiation. The table shows that the evidence for a radiation-related effect is confined to those with a dose above 100 millisievert. Below this dose the number of deaths was 7,657 compared with an expected 7,595 – the difference of 62 is too small to have meaning statistically and is consistent with no effect due to radiation.

Table 5 Mortality from solid cancers between 1950 and 2000 among the survivors of Hiroshima and Nagasaki with measured doses, from Preston et al [19, Table 3].

Dose range (millisievert)	Survivors	Survivor deaths		Extra risk per 1,000
		actual	expected	
<5	38,507	4,270	4,282	−2.0 to 1.4
5 to 100	29,960	3,387	3,313	0.0 to 3.5
100 to 200	5,949	732	691	3.5 to 12.5
200 to 500	6,380	815	736	9 to 18
500 to 1,000	3,426	483	378	25 to 37
1,000 to 2,000	1,764	326	191	63 to 83
>2,000	625	114	56	72 to 108
All	86,611	10,127	9,647	5.0 to 5.2

In conclusion, these data show that there is an effective threshold at 100 millisievert for an acute dose. We can think of this threshold level as distinguishing the intermediate dose range, where there is an effect, from the low dose range where the effect is too small to be measurable. The threshold might be as high as 200 millisievert, as given by the leukaemia data, but use of the 100 millisievert figure is more conservative. The point is that there are no data, in this or any other study, that show that there is a measurable risk of cancer for a single dose below this level. There are always uncertainties, but the margin of error in this case is about 1 in 1,000, an effect on life expectancy of 2 weeks. This level of risk is so low compared with the natural occurrence of cancer that it cannot be detected, even in this 50-year-long study of nearly 100,000 people exposed to the detonation of two nuclear bombs. Finally, the established repair mechanisms should be effective in this low range at least, so we expect there to be no risk at all, that is no loss of life expectancy, even if it could be measured.

The boundary between an intermediate and a high acute dose is at about 2,000 millisievert. Above this, early cell death becomes increasingly likely from a single dose; below it, cell death is less likely. In the intermediate range there are well established links between radiation and cancer, although, even there, radiation is usually a relatively minor cause.

Medical diagnostic scans

Ionising radiation has been used for clinical imaging in hospitals and dental surgeries for well over a century, and the doses delivered to patients in such scans are very small compared with the threshold of 100 millisievert.[32] Historically, scans using ionising radiation were based exclusively on X-rays. Beams of these photons suitable for medical imaging may be produced, either directly from beams of electrons, or from within atoms or

---

[32] Radiation scans are quite different to those that use MRI or ultrasound. MRI does involve nuclear spin but in an entirely passive way that has nothing to do with ionising radiation.

nuclei. X-rays do not *remember* where they came from and their effect does not depend on the source, except to the extent that it affects the energy and intensity. Traditional X-ray pictures are taken with a beam of photons generated by electrons focussed onto a small spot on a metal target such as tungsten, essentially in the way that Röntgen used when he discovered X-rays.

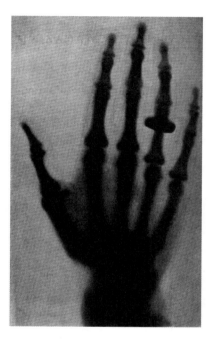

Figure 11   An X-ray image of a hand with ring (printed in McClures Magazine, April 1896).

Such a picture simply shows the directions in which X-rays are absorbed between this source spot and the film or detector. There are no lenses or mirrors – the image is just a shadow. Use of X-rays of medium energy picks out the high Z of calcium in bone or tooth, which absorbs strongly, in contrast to the mix of carbon, hydrogen and oxygen in normal tissue, which have low Z and are nearly transparent. A classic picture is shown in Figure 11. So that it is not faint or spotty the radiation exposure has to provide a large enough number of absorbed photons in each element or pixel of the picture to overcome noise – that is statistical fluctuations. Even with old and inefficient equipment a dose of less than 0.02 millisievert is often sufficient for this purpose, many powers of 10 below the 100 millisievert threshold.

Many of the features that a doctor would like to find are not shown in this kind of image – for instance the pattern of blood vessels. An effective trick dating from the 1920s solves this problem by using a contrast agent – in the case of blood vessels, iodine, an element with high atomic number ($Z = 53$) that absorbs X-rays strongly. The patient is injected with a solution containing iodine and images are taken before and afterwards. (This is normal stable iodine, not the radioactive isotope.) The iodine makes for large differences in absorption, which picks out the blood vessels very clearly. An example of a pair of such images and their difference is shown in Figure 12. The digital subtraction provides an excellent picture of the blood vessels.

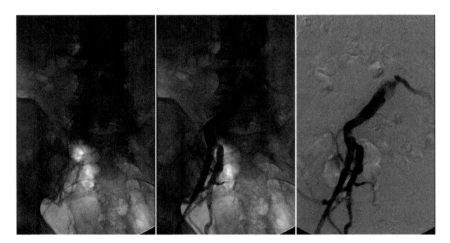

Figure 12 X-ray images of the pelvis and lower spine. On the left is an initial image; in the centre is the same region after injection of iodine as a contrast agent; on the right is an image formed by digital subtraction of the other two, clearly showing the main artery. [Images reproduced by kind permission of Medical Physics and Clinical Engineering, Oxford Radcliffe Hospitals NHS Trust.]

The same trick can be used to make images of the gut. In that case barium ($Z = 56$) is the contrast agent. Barium sulphate is a harmless chalky material, insoluble in water, that can be swallowed and quickly lines the stomach wall. Subtraction of images taken before and afterwards gives high contrast pictures of the whole digestive system.

Modern scans give rise to a higher radiation dose because they give three-dimensional information with much finer detail than is visible in Figure 11. This improved picture quality involves a much larger number of picture-elements,[33] each with a low noise requirement and therefore large number of photons. Although modern scanners make more efficient use of radiation with better detection, filtering and screening, the radiation dose may still be 1 or 2 millisievert per scan. This is larger than for a simple projective X-ray, but still quite small compared with 100 millisievert, the threshold of damage discussed earlier.

Nuclear medicine

It is possible to make images that show what tissue is doing. These are called functional images and are often clinically more interesting than simple anatomical images. Functional imaging is possible with MRI too. An example using radiation is shown in Figure 14. Typically such images incur doses in the range of 1–2 millisievert. The patient is injected with a specially prepared drug, which finds its way in the bloodstream preferentially to sites of abnormal blood vessel development or high metabolic activity, where its presence can be imaged.

This works because molecules of the injected drug are labelled with a radioactive isotope of an atom and as these decay inside the body the emitted radiation passes outside to be detected by special detectors. These can then pinpoint where the decay occurred. The resulting map of nuclear decay positions shows

---

[33] The picture-elements are called *pixels* and *voxels* for a two-dimensional and three-dimensional picture, respectively.

where the drug has accumulated and, therefore, where a cancerous tumour with its anomalous activity is located.

(a) SPECT   **(b) PET**

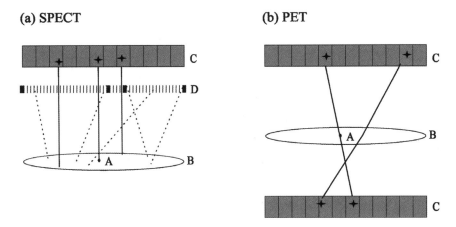

Figure 13   Illustrations of how in SPECT and PET radioactive decays at points like A in a body B emit gamma rays whose line of flight can be located through the signals, shown as stars, appearing in detectors C.

There are two methods that are widely used, called SPECT (single photon emission computed tomography) and PET (positron emission tomography). How the positions of the decaying nuclei are determined in each case is illustrated in Figure 13.

In SPECT the radioactive isotope is usually technetium-99m, which decays emitting one gamma ray of 140 keV.[34] The line of the detected radiation is fixed by the direction of the holes in a special lead collimator plate D, which blocks radiation at other angles from entering the detector C. The camera comprises the lead plate and the detector, as a unit, and during the scan this is moved along and around the patient.

---

[34] The *m*, appended to the isotope name, just indicates that it is an excited state.

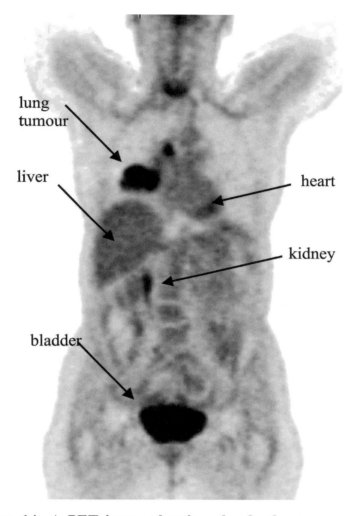

Figure 14 A PET image showing clearly the presence of a tumour on the lung. There is also an accumulation of the reagent in the bladder. [Image reproduced by kind permission of Medical Physics and Clinical Engineering, Oxford Radcliffe Hospitals NHS Trust.]

For PET the usual isotope chosen is fluorine-19, which emits a positron. This travels a millimetre or so, stops and annihilates with a simple atomic electron into *two* 511 keV gamma rays, back-to-back in a straight line. There is no plate and the line of the radiation is fixed by the detection of two simultaneous signals.

PET gives the better quality images of the two but is more technically demanding, although in both the contrast associated with the selective concentration of the isotope can be outstanding. This concentration decreases over time by radioactive decay and by natural removal from the body by excretion. The decay half-life of technetium-99m is 6 hours; that of fluorine-19 just 2 hours. So patients receiving a SPECT scan continue to be irradiated for a longer time afterwards than those receiving PET – but there is a stronger argument in favour of PET. With SPECT most of the radiation must be absorbed in the lead sheet shown in Figure 13. In fact only a rather small fraction passes through the holes to be detected, while the rest contributes nothing. So for an image of similar quality the patient receives a greater radiation dose with SPECT than with PET. With finer holes the SPECT image is improved but the dose is higher – there is a compromise. In practice SPECT is more widely used because it is cheaper and easier than PET.

At first sight nuclear medicine may seem alarming – the patient is made radioactive! However, the radiation is specifically chosen to escape from the body with minimal absorption – and therefore contributing the least dose. This is quite different to an X-ray image where the contrast arises from the absorption itself through its differences in various tissues.

The gamma rays of PET and SPECT, with energies of 511 keV and 140 keV respectively, have ranges of about 10 cm in the body. By sparing use of the isotope, the dose is kept in the range of a few millisievert, depending on the examination. Such restraint makes the images rather grainy and noisy, as shown in the example, Figure 14. Doses given in clinical practice are so far below the 100 millisievert threshold that there may be circumstances in which it would be beneficial to increase the exposure to get a clearer picture. Some authorities (Joint Report by the French National Academies [21, 22]) think that current practice is unjustifiably cautious.

The average annual dose of ionising radiation experienced by the general public has risen slightly in recent decades because of the greater use of medical imaging with ionising radiation. This increase has been less than it would otherwise have been because of improvements in detection efficiency. Generally the benefits to health are acknowledged and are complementary to the use of MRI and ultrasound. Nowadays diagnostic images frequently use data taken by more than one method to form a fused image, combining, for example, the discrimination of PET with the precision of MRI. The risks of nuclear medicine are insignificant compared with the health benefits that are obvious to all.

People irradiated at Chernobyl

Among those irradiated at Chernobyl, two groups were particularly badly affected: those who received exceptionally high radiation doses, and those who ingested radioactive iodine and contracted thyroid cancer. Others include those who took part in the clean up, the locals who were relocated and others who lived further afield in neighbouring states and regions.

The fate of those 237 who received the highest doses is shown in Figure 9b on page 81. These were the firemen and other workers who fought the reactor fire in the immediate aftermath of the accident. Of these, 28 died within a few weeks with the symptoms of acute radiation sickness. In the following 18 years a further 19 died from a variety of causes – a similar number would have died in the normal course of events, although it is not possible to be sure that radiation was not the cause of death in any instance.

Thyroid cancer

Among the many radioactive fission products of uranium is iodine-131. So at the time of the Chernobyl accident the reactor contained a significant quantity, all of which vaporised readily in

the heat of the fire – iodine boils at 184°C. This radioactive
iodine dispersed in the atmosphere and some was then inhaled
directly by local people and farm animals, or was otherwise
absorbed into the food chain, often in the form of milk or
vegetables. Although the amount of iodine in the body is less
than 1 part in 2 million, it accumulates quickly in the thyroid
gland, whether it is radioactive or not – chemical and biological
processes are quite insensitive to the nuclear properties of
elements so all isotopes are treated similarly. Any radioactive
iodine absorbed in the thyroid decays with a half-life of eight
days and so is soon gone. However, the highly concentrated
energy dose is responsible for a legacy of latent damage that may
generate cancer some years later. It has long been known that if
potassium iodide tablets are taken for several weeks following a
radiation accident, the take-up of the radioactive form of the
iodine is diluted thereby, and the radiation dose is reduced. The
need to distribute iodine tablets in the event of an accident was
well known early in the Cold War years and was a standard
element of Civil Defence at that time – the tablets being cheap
and easy to keep. The recommended dose is 130 mg per day, and
half that for children. There are no side effects at these doses,
whether taken as potassium iodide or potassium iodate [23], and
their availability need not be controlled by medical prescription.
A major release of radioactive iodine-131 into the environment
occurred as a result of the nuclear accident at Windscale in 1957
[24]. However, the release was a thousand times smaller than
that at Chernobyl so that more has been learnt from studying the
latter.

Children are more at risk than adults as their thyroid is
developing and their diet is normally rich in milk. The incidence
of thyroid cancer amongst children in the neighbouring countries
after Chernobyl is shown in Table 6. Not all of these 4,837 cases
are radiation-induced – the incidence would have been about a
tenth, but for the accident. Radiation doses to the thyroid varied
from tens of millisievert to 3,000-4,000 millisievert. Most of the

sufferers have received therapy successfully[35] but there have been a number of recorded deaths – 15 cases up to 2002 [12, p.16] .

Table 6   The number of cases of thyroid cancer in the neighbourhood of Chernobyl diagnosed between 1986 and 2002 by country and age of exposure [13, Table 5].

Age at exposure	Number of cases			
	Belarus	Russia	Ukraine	Total
<14	1,711	349	1,762	3,822
15–17	299	134	582	1,015
Total	2,010	483	2,344	4,837

At Chernobyl the authorities were slow to distribute iodine tablets. The short half-life of iodine-131 suggests that, to have any effect, the tablets should be given for just a few weeks following an accident, for by then that the radioactive iodine has decayed. This may seem obvious, but a recent large-scale study of thyroid cancer at Chernobyl by Cardis [25] has shown that this is not the case! Extra normal iodine, even given much later, was found to reduce the incidence of thyroid cancer by a factor of three – presumably by boosting the development of a healthy thyroid gland with consequentially improved immunity against cancer development.[36] This is an important new observation, as noted by Boice [26]. It suggests that protection mechanisms continue to be active during the latent period, perhaps years later,

---

[35]   Radiotherapy for thyroid cancer often employs brachytherapy (see page 114) using the very same radioactive isotope of iodine. The therapy involves maximising the uptake of radioiodine by the tumour to induce cell death rather than cancer. Alternatively external gamma ray radiotherapy may be used.

[36]   The US Food and Drug Administration recommends a diet with a daily intake of 0.15 milligrams of iodine to promote a healthy thyroid, either naturally or by the addition of iodised salt to food. The concentration of iodine in such salt varies from 10 (UK) to 50 ppm (US).

between the exposure to the radiation and the appearance of the cancer. It raises the question whether the incidence of other cancers may also be reduced by general good health during latency.

A second effect found in the same study by Cardis is linked to the natural iodine content of the local diet. In the regions around Chernobyl that are poor in natural iodine, the incidence of thyroid cancer has been greater than in the regions where it is richer. It is reasonable to suppose that the take-up of the radioisotope is enhanced where the thyroid was previously starved of natural iodine. As most of the regions around Chernobyl are iodine-poor, this would have contributed to the high incidence of cancer. If a future accident occurred in a region with an adequate pre-existing level of iodine, the incidence of cancer would then be much lower than found at Chernobyl. Although the findings of Cardis [25] need confirmation, there are important implications here for public health, and the prognosis for thyroid cancer in the event of a future accident is encouraging. If thyroid health is maintained by sufficient intake of iodine under normal circumstances, the incidence of cancer might be substantially reduced, compared with Chernobyl.

Other cancers at Chernobyl

In principle the Hiroshima and Nagasaki survivor data give the cancer mortality for those suffering a given whole-body radiation dose. If the dose profile of those affected by Chernobyl were known, the number of cases of leukaemia and solid cancers expected over 50 years could be predicted without the need to assume any particular shape for the dose-damage curve, such as whether it is linear or not. However, this profile is not known at all well. The best general estimate for the accumulated doses is given in Table 7. This distinguishes the liquidators who were drafted in to clear up, those who were evacuated after a few days, those who live in the immediate zone and those who live further afield. It shows that a large number of people received a dose of less than 100 millisievert, often over a period of many years. No excess cancers, other than thyroid, have been demonstrated, as is to be expected given the results from the Hiroshima and Nagasaki survivors. The far larger effect of other causes of cancers makes any contribution from radiation undetectable.

Table 7 The extra radiation dose, totalled over the years, received by affected populations as a result of the Chernobyl accident (excluding cases of acute radiation sickness and thyroid cancer) [12, p.14]. The final column shows the corresponding annual dose.

	Years	Population	Total dose	Annual dose
			millisievert	
Liquidators	1986–1989	600,000	~100	~25
Evacuees	1986	116,000	33	33
Residents of 'strict control' zones	1986–2005	270,000	>50	>2.5
Residents of other 'contaminated' areas	1986–2005	5,000,000	10 to 20	0.5 to 1

Nevertheless it is still quite easy to compute the collective dose from the numbers in Table 7 – it is 150,000 man-sievert. *If* the chance of death could be reckoned at 5% per man-sievert, as suggested by the International Commission for Radiological Protection [27, p.55, para. 87] the number of deaths *would be* 7,500. But there are no data to support this at all, and it relies essentially on the assumption of linearity. It can be argued that such use of LNT was not justified for blood donation, and that it is not applicable here. In fact, in its latest recommendations, ICRP103, the Commission cautions against such calculations [27, p.13, para. k]:

> *calculation of the number of cancer deaths based on collective doses from trivial individual doses should be avoided.*

Nevertheless, the IAEA 2006 Report did not follow this advice when discussing the number of cancer deaths at Chernobyl and stated [12, p.16]

> This *might* *eventually* represent *up to* four thousand fatal cancers in addition to the approximately 100,000 fatal cancers to be expected due to all other causes in this population. [emphasis added]

It offers no basis or data for this vague statement, but it can only be based on LNT, since no cancers were observed. The actual number is simply not known. Even based on the IAEA number, the loss of life expectancy (the detriment), would be very small compared with the effect of other fatal cancers, as the IAEA remarks.

However, the IAEA Report also gives a broader and more informative picture [12, p.7].

> *Apart from the dramatic increase in thyroid cancer incidence among those exposed at a young age, there is no clearly demonstrated increase in the incidence of solid cancers or leukaemia due to radiation in the most affected populations. There was, however, an increase in psychological problems among the affected population, compounded by insufficient communication about radiation effects and by the social disruption and economic depression that followed the break-up of the Soviet Union.*

On page 13 it compares the total doses at Chernobyl accumulated over many years with those that occur naturally in many parts of the world.

> *The average effective doses for the general population of 'contaminated' areas accumulated in 1986–2005 were estimated to be between 10 and 30 millisievert in various administrative regions of Belarus, Russia and Ukraine. In the areas of strict radiological control, the average dose was around 50 millisievert and more. Some residents received up to several hundred millisievert. It should be noted that the average doses received by*

residents of the territories 'contaminated' by Chernobyl fallout are generally lower than those received by people who live in some areas of high natural background radiation in India, Iran, Brazil and China (100–200 millisievert in 20 years).

The point is that the corresponding *annual* doses are very small, as given in the final column of Table 7. Note that the quotation marks around the description *contaminated* are in the original report. Evidently this description is no longer considered generally appropriate.

Much of the concern about radiation safety has centred on genetic effects. Whereas cancer might affect individuals, any genetic effects of radiation might be passed on to later generations. The IAEA Report addresses the question [12, p. 19]:

Have there been, or will there be, any long term inherited or reproductive effects as a result of Chernobyl?

Because of the relatively low dose levels to which the populations of the Chernobyl-affected regions were exposed, there is no evidence or any likelihood of observing decreased fertility among males or females in the general population as a direct result of radiation exposure. These doses are also unlikely to have any major effect on the number of stillbirths, adverse pregnancy outcomes or delivery complications or the overall health of children.

Birth rates may be lower in 'contaminated' areas because of concern about having children (this issue is obscured by the very high rate of medical abortions) and the fact that many younger people have moved away. No discernable (sic) increase in hereditary effects caused by radiation is expected based on the low risk coefficients estimated by UNSCEAR (2001) or in previous reports on Chernobyl health effects. Since 2000, there has been no new evidence provided to change this conclusion.

There has been a modest but steady increase in reported congenital malformations in both 'contaminated' and 'uncontaminated' areas of Belarus since 1986. This does not appear to be radiation-related and may be the result of increased registration.

The IAEA Report has important points to make about social health [12, p.20],

The Chernobyl accident resulted in many people being traumatized by the rapid relocation, the breakdown in social contacts, fear and anxiety about what health effects might result. Are there persistent psychological or mental health problems?

Any traumatic accident or event can cause the incidence of stress symptoms, depression, anxiety (including post-traumatic stress symptoms), and medically unexplained physical symptoms. Such effects have also been reported in Chernobyl-exposed populations. Three studies found that exposed populations had anxiety levels that were twice as high as controls, and they were 3-4 times more likely to report multiple unexplained physical symptoms and subjective poor health than were unaffected control groups. In general, although the psychological consequences found in Chernobyl exposed populations are similar to those in atomic bombing survivors, residents near the Three Mile Island nuclear power plant accident, and those who experienced toxic exposures at work or in the environment, the context in which the Chernobyl accident occurred makes the findings difficult to interpret because of the complicated series of events unleashed by the accident, the multiple extreme stresses and culture-specific ways of expressing distress.

The IAEA 2006 Report [12] continues by commenting on the real consequences of the unfortunate official action and media reaction to Chernobyl.

In addition, individuals in the affected populations were officially categorized as 'sufferers', and came to be

known colloquially as 'Chernobyl victims', a term that was soon adopted by the mass media. This label, along with the extensive government benefits earmarked for evacuees and residents of the contaminated territories, had the effect of encouraging individuals to think of themselves fatalistically as invalids. It is known that people's perceptions — even if false — can affect the way they feel and act. Thus, rather than perceiving themselves as 'survivors', many of those people have come to think of themselves as helpless, weak and lacking control over their future.

The obsession with safety, or rather a simple fear of radiation, lead blindly to social damage that was much worse. It is known that belief in ill-health can be self fulfilling [2]. The IAEA Report's conclusion, expressed in connection with Chernobyl, should be extended to all information about different aspects of radiation.

Renewed efforts at risk communication, providing the public and key professionals with accurate information about the health and mental health consequences of the disaster, should be undertaken.

Although the number of casualties at Chernobyl due to radiation is uncertain, it is small on the scale of global disasters, some of which are listed in Table 8. Was the accident at Chernobyl a major global physical disaster? The numbers suggest not – even if the LNT-based estimates are used.

For any modern nuclear reactor with a containment vessel and properly designed stable operating conditions, the likelihood of an accident like Chernobyl is tiny. Properly trained operating crews, honest public education and free provision of iodine tablets in homes would ensure that the risks arising from such an incident, even if it did occur, would be much smaller than at Chernobyl. Even as it was, the Chernobyl nuclear accident was much less serious than the Bhopal chemical disaster in which over 3,800 people lost their lives. But both accidents were small and local compared with those that may be anticipated as a result of climate change. For the Soviet Union the Chernobyl accident was indeed a disaster; but a socio-economic and political one. Physically, on a world scale it was a small accident.

Table 8 Some major man-made chemical, radiation and other disasters (excluding other large numbers for wars, genocides, poor sanitation and health care).

Date	Agent	Incident	Deaths
Aug 1945	nuclear	Hiroshima and Nagasaki	100,000+
Feb 1945	chemical	Dresden	35,000+
Dec 1984	chemical	Bhopal	3,800+
Sept 2001	terrorism	World Trade Centre 9/11	2,996
Aug 2005	climate?	Katrina	900+
April 1986	nuclear	Chernobyl	~50+
Feb 2009	climate?	Australian bush fires	209
July 1976	chemical	Seveso	0+
Mar 1979	nuclear	Three Mile Island	0

Why, at the time, was there such an over-reaction to what happened at Chernobyl? An indication comes from a recent admission published by the Swedish Radiation Protection Authority in an article in the Stockholm daily press [28], signed by (amongst others) Dr Lars-Erik Holm, chairman of the International Commission for Radiological Protection (ICRP). In the article the directors of the Authority admit that they set the immediate post-Chernobyl safety regulation so restrictive that no one in Sweden should receive even 1 millisievert of radiation per year from eating meat affected by Chernobyl fallout. They admit that in practice this reduced doses to only a few percent of a millisievert. Consequently 78% of all reindeer meat was destroyed at great cost to taxpayers and adversity for the reindeer herders.

The thinking behind this intervention level was that the individual risk should be low enough that the consumer would not need to worry at all about what he or she bought in the shops. In the article they wrote,

> *Perhaps we took on too great a responsibility for the individual consumer.*

That would seem to be true – they did not understand human nature. It does not help to apply drastic regulations and then tell the population that they are safe and should not worry. Fortunately the population is not so phlegmatic. If people feel that they are being managed without a fair proportion being fully informed, they will over-react and even panic. In this case the result was that many people were frightened and a large quantity of good meat was destroyed. But there was more. They also wrote in the article,

> *One known problem of ionising radiation is that for many people, and also for the media, the phrase itself evokes a sense of danger. It has for many years now been difficult, from a strict radiation protection point of view, to claim that small radiation doses are harmless....*

So it would seem that their misplaced belief in LNT and lack of confident leadership left the authorities themselves panicking and making over-defensive decisions, which they then regretted.

Earlier, in 1980, following the Three Mile Island accident, the Swedish people had already voted to phase out nuclear power. It was not until February 2009 that the government announced that this decision would be reversed and new nuclear reactors built.

Chapter 7 Multiple Doses of Radiation

Distributed doses

A radiation dose may refer to a single occasion of irradiation, or it may describe irradiation over a period, either continuously or as a sequence of separate exposures. These are different in principle – an acute dose may be measured in millisievert and a chronic dose in millisievert per month. If a radiation dose is given over a period or continuously, how does its effect compare with that of the same total dose given as a single burst?

A similar question can be asked about place rather than time. How does the effect of a dose of radiation given all in one place differ from that of the same energy dose spread more widely over the anatomy of an individual? Or even distributed between a number of individuals?

The data discussed in Chapter 6 concerned an acute dose given all at one time. The response to doses that are distributed raises questions involving linearity that we discussed in Chapter 5. If the linear no-threshold (LNT) picture were applicable, the probability of developing cancer would be the same whether a given energy dose (in joules) was focussed onto a smaller or larger mass of tissue. More generally the damage per joule of radiation energy would be the same, whether spread over many individuals, spread over the body of one individual, or delivered over a period of time. If that were true, it would be appropriate to base safety regulations on collective dose – and such regulations would be relatively simple to apply. But this is not just a matter of convenience. Does evidence justify such simple picture, or not?

For a given energy dose the damage due to different types of radiation varies, as described in principle by the relative biological effectiveness (RBE) discussed on page 47. The reason why electrons and photons are least damaging is that the energy that they deposit is quite spread out. In a flux of charged particles the situation is different, and each particle makes a track with a density of collision events along it that depends on its charge z and speed v, as z^2/v^2. This is called the linear energy transfer (LET).[37] So an alpha ($z = 2$) has four times the LET of a proton ($z = 1$) of the same speed. At energies normally encountered in the environment, electrons are very fast (being light) and protons and alpha particles are slow (being heavy). So the LET for protons is much higher than for electrons, but much less than for alphas.

Neutral radiation – photons and neutrons – deposit no energy directly, but photons kick electrons out of atoms and neutrons knock nuclei about. These behave like a sequence of electrons and low velocity nuclei, respectively – and so have spatial distributions corresponding to low and high LET, respectively. The upshot is that the LET is the principal distinction between types of radiation, and may be expected to determine the RBE – given the indiscriminate effect of deposited radiation, RBE cannot really depend much on anything else.

If LNT was applicable, we should expect RBE to be the same for photons and all radiation – that is unity. In the non-linear picture, the local energy density of high LET is seen to impose a greater load on local repair mechanisms than the greater spatial uniformity of low LET. This argument suggests a spatial scale – if the repair services were available at any distance, there would be no LET dependence. This spatial scale[38] typically extends to groups of cells, signalling and cooperating together – or failing to do so when collectively overloaded. This distance scale appears as a range for dose integration in the spatial picture, rather as the repair time appears in the time domain. Both are characteristic features of a non-linear response.

---

[37] Note that the word *linear,* as used in LET, simply means *along the line* – that is the track of the incident charge. The word *linear,* as used elsewhere, has the meaning described on page 55. These two meanings are quite distinct.

[38] Study of the local deposited energy density is called micro-dosimetry. We have no space here to follow this active and important field. The main ideas are discussed by Simmons and Watt [29].

How does the biological damage vary when a dose is spread out over a day, a month, a year or a lifetime? Simple ideas of repair mechanisms lead us to expect that, given enough time, accumulated damage should be eliminated. The important numbers are the repair time and the damage threshold. The picture is therefore like this – if the dose accumulated within any repair time remains below threshold, no permanent damage is incurred. This is what we might expect from the discussion in Chapter 5. If there are a number of repair mechanisms, there may be several repair times. But these are just ideas – the real story must be left to observational data. Single incidents such as the bombs of 1945, or Chernobyl, cannot provide an answer on this question. Evidence for the effect of large multiple or chronic radiation doses is needed and this is discussed in the rest of this chapter.

Cancer therapy

Arguably the most compelling evidence comes from a century of clinical experience with cancer radiotherapy. We begin with some explanation of the use of radiotherapy in the treatment of cancer.

A cancerous tumour is a group of cells that grows without respect for the organism as a whole. Left unchecked, it develops at the expense of the normal functioning of the body, monopolising its goods and services. If the patient is to survive, the cells of the tumour must die before it colonises and spreads (metastasises). If it has already spread, palliative treatment may be designed to extend life for the patient by slowing the growth of the cancer. Otherwise, death of the tumour cells is the aim, and this has to be achieved without irreversibly damaging adjacent tissue and organs that are otherwise healthy. The broad options are surgery, radiotherapy, chemotherapy and focussed ultrasound – or a combination of these. The stage that the cancer has reached and its location largely determine the choice of treatment.

What is needed is a precise knowledge of the location of the tumour and its three-dimensional shape, and then a means of targeting the dose so as to minimise peripheral damage while delivering a terminal blow to the cells of the tumour itself. This calls for a method of dose delivery that can match the shape of the treated volume with a sharply defined edge, that is a high gradient of dose, able to kill cells in one region but spare those a short distance away.

In radiotherapy the energetic radiation may be delivered in a number of ways: by an external beam of gamma radiation, by an external beam of electrons or heavy ions, or by a surgically implanted radioactive source, a treatment called *brachytherapy*.

Modern external gamma ray beams are generated by electrons, whereas earlier ones often used an external radioactive source, such as cobalt-60. Surface cancers may be treated with electron beams or gamma rays with less energy because less penetration is required – that is a less demanding application. It is the deeper cancers that pose difficulties.

Whatever the source used in the clinical treatment, during the initial radiotherapy planning phase, a three-dimensional scanned image of the tumour and its surrounding tissue is used to map and optimise the delivery of the energy dose. However, unlike a beam of light, charged ions or electrons, a beam of gamma radiation cannot be focussed – such lenses and mirrors do not exist. As a result when gamma rays are used for therapy, the targeting is poor and much of the energy is spilled in the wrong tissue. Some goes beyond the tumour, some is absorbed in healthy tissue before it gets there and quite a lot is scattered sideways out of the beam, as shown diagrammatically in Figure 15. This means that such treatment plans are not ideal.

The Report of the Royal College of Radiologists [30] records that the practice of radiotherapy has developed empirically rather than as an exact science. Its early successful use was often for superficial cancers, and the treatment of deep cancers has always

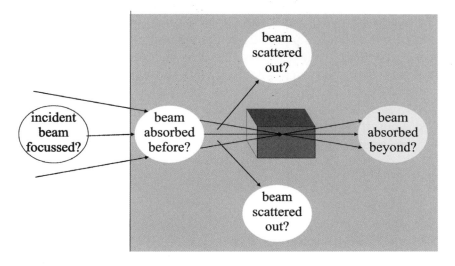

Figure 15 A diagrammatic sketch of the radiotherapy of a deep-seated tumour. The volume to be irradiated uniformly is indicated by the heavily shaded box within tissue that should be spared, shown lightly shaded.

presented the greatest challenge. Extra depth penetration is achieved by using higher energy gamma rays of several MeV.

Such radiation delivers a flux of energy that builds up below the skin surface and then falls off sufficiently slowly with depth that some of it reaches as far as the tumour. To enhance the energy deposited there, the treatment is given from a number of different directions that overlap in the region of the tumour. The geometry is improved further by shaping the transverse size of the beam with computer-controlled lead collimator fingers.

An example of a radiotherapy plan for treatment of the prostate is shown in Figure 16. Although this is only a slice of what is a three-dimensional task, it is sufficient to explain the situation. Percentage contour lines of dose relative to the maximum are shown. The inner 97% contour matches the region to be treated, avoiding the region of the sensitive rectum, but only by a few percent. The 30% contour shows that the various different beam directions used in the plan have a significant effect on the peripheral dose suffered. Even the 50% dose contour (shown as a thick line) extends far out from the tumour into the peripheral tissue. Evidently the ratio of dose to the tumour and to the healthy tissue is less than a factor two in this case.

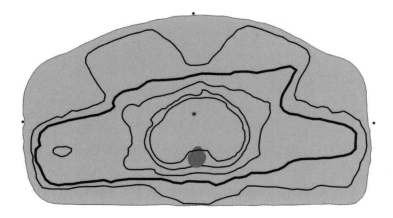

Figure 16 A section of a treatment plan for radiotherapy of the prostate, showing dose contours 97%, 90%, 70%, 50% (heavier line) and 30% of the peak dose at the position of the asterisk (*). The rectum is shown heavily shaded. The three dots on the surface of the anatomy represent registration marks. [From an image by kind permission of Medical Physics and Clinical Engineering, Oxford Radcliffe Hospitals NHS Trust.]

Although such targeting seems poor, these treatments are given in every major hospital, usually, but not always, with life-saving consequences. This success relies essentially on the non-linearity of the dose-damage curve – while the difference in dose between the tumour and healthy tissue may be less than a factor two, the ratio of cell mortality is much greater. As an illustration, the steep slope of a non-linear curve, such as Figure 9 on page 81, suggests that a 10% difference in dose might be responsible for a factor two in cell mortality, if the right dose range is chosen. The downside is that successful treatment is highly sensitive to any small change in the dose given, because the curve is so steep. In practice, doses need to be controlled to a percent or so. Too little, and the tumour will not be controlled; too much, and nearby organs will be permanently damaged. The Royal College of Radiologists Report [30] says, in connection with treatment of the spinal cord as an example,

> *Dose-response relationships for tumour control are steep and a 4-5% dose increase might lead to a 10% increase in probability of tumour control. Yet 0.5-1% increase in the risk of treatment related paraplegia is, for many radiation oncologists, unacceptable.*

Failure to calibrate and control the dose is the most frequent cause of radiotherapy accidents when these occur.

Fractionation

Table 9   Some recommended dose and fractionation procedures [30].

Cancer	Fractions	Total dose	Interval
bladder	30×2 gray	60 gray	5 times per week
breast	16×2.7 gray	42.5 gray	5 times per week
armpit	15×2.7 gray	40 gray	5 times per week
glioma	30×2 gray	60 gray	5 times per week
cervical	25×1.8 gray	45 gray	5 times per week
lung	36×1.8 gray	54 gray	in 12 days
prostate	39×2 gray	78 gray	5 times per week

The first treatment by radiotherapy was given in 10 daily doses over the period 24 November to 3 December 1896. The reason for this protracted treatment was instrumental. When equipment improved, therapy could be given as a large single dose. But after 20 years it was concluded that this was much less effective. Today recommended treatment plans, selected in the light of experience, call for all radiotherapy treatment to be given as a number of treatment *fractions*, coincidentally spread much as in 1896. Detailed practice varies, but some figures recommended for the UK are given in Table 9. The schedules range from 12 to 40 days. A disadvantage of fractionation is that it prolongs the treatment by requiring many hospital visits, which reduces patient throughput, increases costs, and does not help the patient experience.

Given an appreciation of repair effects it is straightforward to understand, at a simple level at least, how fractionation works. The daily gap between fractions or partial doses gives time for simple DNA repairs in the healthy tissue – repair times are known from biological studies to be several hours, depending on tissue and age. Within the tumour where the dose level is higher, there is a greater chance of cell death in each fraction. So with successive fractions cells in the peripheral regions just manage to recover each time, while the cells in the tumour suffer progressive attrition. More subtly, as the treatment continues, apoptosis clears away the cell wreckage within the tumour and the oxygen concentration there starts to recover. This leads to an increase in the oxidative biological damage to the tumour in later fractions of the treatment. Otherwise, initially at least, the low oxygen concentration in an active tumour makes it less radiation sensitive than the healthy tissue, and this has a counter-productive influence in radiotherapy.

So the experience is that the efficacy of radiotherapy depends on dividing the treatment into fractions, applied over a period of time rather than being given all at once – so the Superposition Principle fails and the effect is non-linear. The accumulated dose to the tumour, 40 to 80 gray as given in Table 9, is such that peripheral healthy tissue receives about 30 gray over a month of treatment – far greater than it could survive if administered as a single dose.[39] Without the non-linearity of the dose-response curve radiotherapy would not be effective. Although the peripheral tissue absorbing these high fractionated doses may recover its function, there may be some permanent damage in the

---

[39] Recall that the dose units gray and sievert are effectively identical.

form of scarring. This is one reason why a repeat course of radiotherapy treatment is often not recommended if the first is unsuccessful.

Radiation doses used in radiotherapy are high, and it is to be expected that, in addition to treating the cancer concerned, the radiation itself should occasionally initiate new disease. In principle sufficient data are available to measure this, because the number of treated patients is very large. However, confounding effects make such studies difficult. Some convincing evidence is based on the incidence of heart disease among women who received therapy to the right breast compared with those whose treatment was to the left breast [31]. Poor targeting of radiation treatment in the 1970s and 1980s was such that the dose to the heart was greater for radiotherapy treatment of the left breast than the right. Any spurious influences such as affluence, diet or smoking are the same for both groups. In the study of 20,871 women the number of deaths from cardiac disease 15 or more years after treatment were noted and separated according to whether they had radiotherapy or not, and whether they had a tumour in the left breast or the right breast. The result shows an increase of heart disease mortality for those who received radiotherapy to the left breast compared with those who received it to the right breast, by a factor 1.25. The doses to the heart are not reported but could have been in the range of 1 sievert per day,. Taken with the measured increase in heart disease of 10% for an acute dose of 1 sievert, reported by Shimizu [20], it could be argued that this result suggests that the integration time for radiation damage that leads eventually to cancer is about a couple of days.

This time is very imprecise, but it is important because it suggests that the repair time for damage that leads eventually to cancer is in the same range as the repair time that leads to cell death. This does not support a picture in which latent cancer builds up progressively without correction, and neither do the observations of the effect of late iodine on the incidence of thyroid cancer reported by Cardis [25], discussed on page 101.

The targeting of radiotherapy is better today than it was in the 1970s, and research is in hand to improve it much further through the use of focussed energetic ion beams in place of photons [32, 33]. Such beams, for example carbon ions, scatter less than gammas and have a rather well defined longitudinal range so that a much larger fraction of the energy can be deposited within the tumour. Treatment with these ions will provide a more tightly defined and heavily damaged region with less peripheral dose. To benefit from this improved targeting, better alignment of the tumour and beam, to track cardiac and respiratory motion for example, is also required. Advances with focussed ultrasound, some involving physically targeted chemotherapy, also promise a brighter future for treatment targeting with other cancer therapies [4].

Doses in the environment

The levels of different radiation exposures that we have discussed are compared in Figure 17 on a common dose scale that runs up the page – note that this is logarithmic. None of these figures is precise to a factor of 2, but it is the factors of 10 that we want to understand. Some exposures are single or acute, some repeated and some continuous. The acute dose levels are shown in the column labelled 'a'. These are the 50% mortality dose (5,500 millisievert, Figure 9), the cancer threshold at 100 millisievert, and the range of dose from a single diagnostic examination (about 0.1 to 3 millisievert). Acute radiation sickness occurs above 5,500 and cancer risks are detectable above 100 mSv, but below that is risk-free, for all intents and purposes.

Other doses are either repeated (a radiotherapy dose in the range 1,000–2,000 millisievert per day) or chronic (natural background at 2 to 5 or more millisievert per year). To compare these with the acute doses, they are shown as doses, accumulated over a month (Figure 17b) and accumulated over a day (Figure 17c). If the repair time is a month, column b is relevant. If the time is a day, then it is column c. From the discussion of the biology the right choice is somewhere between, depending on the tissue concerned and the age of the individual. Radiotherapy treatment effectively assumes a repair time of 1 day. So the choice of a month is conservative, when considering levels of radiation safety.

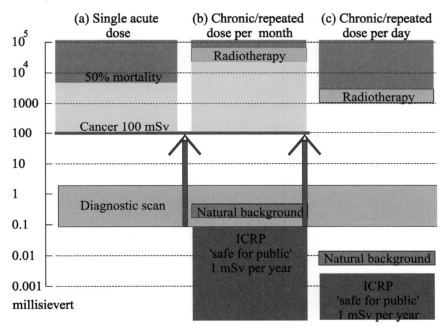

Figure 17 A comparison of chronic and repeated radiation doses (columns b and c) with single acute doses (column a). Also shown is the dose *rate* currently recommended as a safe upper limit for members of the public by ICRP. The comparison with column a is made appropriate for a repair time of a month (column b) and a day (column c). The green arrows indicate the 1000-fold change in safety levels that is suggested by the evidence.

A chronic radiation dose rate of 100 millisievert per month may therefore be considered to be as safe as a single dose of 100 millisievert. Such a rate is less than a radiotherapy dose rate delivered to healthy tissue by a factor 300. Such a factor gives a wide margin over the side effects of scarring and occasional radiation-induced cancers incurred in healthy tissues by radiotherapy.

This suggested safety level for chronic dose rate of 100 millisievert per month is a thousand times larger than the ICRP recommended safety level of 1 millisievert per year, as illustrated in Figure 17. This factor of a thousand is indicated by the green arrows in the figure and is an estimate of the extent to which the current radiation safety regime is over-protective in respect of dose rates.[40] If the repair time is taken to be a day, as the radiotherapy experience suggests, then this factor is even larger. However, the cautious use of a month is appropriate to cover a range of characteristic recovery times. It also matches, or exceeds, a normal convalescent recovery period (p. 70).

There remains the possibility that a chronic low dose rate, experienced year after year, might accumulate a risk with a much longer recovery time or an accumulation of damage with no recovery at all. We need to look at evidence based on large numbers of humans, exposed to radiation over many years.

Radon and lung cancer

Radiotherapy involves high doses of radiation spread out over a few weeks. But what happens when a chronic exposure lasts for years, or even a lifetime? And what is the effect on the incidence of cancer of radiation with a high weighting factor[41] relative to gammas, such as alpha radiation? These are new questions.

Widespread concern was expressed when a source of alpha radiation, polonium-210, was used internally to murder the dissident, Alexander Litvinenko. Such a radioactive source, emitting radiation undetectable outside the body, delivers a

---

[40] In 1951 the safety level recommended by ICRP was set at 12 millisievert per month, since when its recommendations have been tightened by a factor 150. Instead relative to 1951 modern evidence suggests a relaxation by a modest factor six.

[41] See page 47.

highly localised dose to the internal organs where the polonium has been absorbed. This bizarre story caused much public apprehension at the time. One may ask whether there are any similar sources of radiation in the environment, and, if so, whether they carry risks for those who encounter them.

There is a threat of this type from the radioactive gas radon-222, which decays by alpha emission with a half-life of 3.8 days. It occurs naturally in the decay chain of uranium-238 as described in Table 3 on page 43. It is therefore a component of the natural radiation environment, along with gamma rays that escape from rocks and other materials. There is great geographical variability in radon emission, depending on the uranium content of water, soil and rock and whether the radon escapes into the air before it decays.

The concentration of radon actually encountered in homes and workplaces within a region is also variable. As radon is eight times denser than air it accumulates at floor level, and in cellars and mines, unless these are particularly well ventilated. The materials from which the walls and floors of buildings are constructed also affect the radon concentration. As a result the average exposure to radon that an individual receives in his or her life is quite difficult to measure. However, an immense effort has been put into such measurements, and also into studying the correlation of the results with the incidence of lung cancer. Radon concentration is measured in terms of its radioactivity in a volume of air, becquerel per cubic metre ($Bq\ m^{-3}$). The ICRP103 Report [27, p. 16] treats an average of 600 $Bq\ m^{-3}$ in dwellings as equivalent to 10 millisievert per year 'by convention'. It is not clear how firm this equivalence is.

Many populations, for instance in Europe, North America and China, have been studied in this way. The European average exposure has been estimated to be about 59 $Bq\ m^{-3}$, but individuals living in environments with average activity as high as 800 to 1,000 $Bq\ m^{-3}$ have been identified. Some European regions with high values include Devon and Cornwall in the UK, the Czech Republic and the Massif Centrale in France.

National studies have proved inconclusive – that is their data are statistically consistent with no dependence of cancer on the radon environment. Consequently, large combined studies have been undertaken in the hope of establishing what was already established to be a small effect at worst. The most widely quoted of these combined studies is the pan-European study of Darby et al [34], with a subsequent more detailed publication [35]. Its conclusions, based on the combined data from 13 separate national studies, have been summarised by the World Health Organization (WHO) [36]:

> *From the results of (this) study, when a non-smoker is exposed to radon concentrations of 0, 100 and 400 Bq/m³, the risk of lung cancer by age 75 years will be about 4, 5 and 7 in a 1000, respectively. However, for those who smoke, the risk of lung cancer is about 25 times greater, namely 100, 120 and 160 in a 1000, respectively. Most of the radon-induced lung cancer cases occur among smokers.*

It is important to examine carefully what Darby et al established. Their data comprised an assessment of the individual radon environment, at home and at work, over some 30 years for 7,148 individuals, who subsequently did contract lung cancer before the age of 75, and 14,208 individuals, who did not. As noted by WHO the incidence of cancer is dominated by the effect of smoking. Therefore, the question is, what is the *additional* risk of cancer due to radon? This question is reminiscent of the apples and pears problem discussed on page 55. In a linear picture the extra risk from radon is unrelated to smoking, whereas the result from Darby et al quoted by WHO gives the extra risk due to 100 Bq m⁻³ of radon as 0.1% for non-smokers but 2% for smokers. This is a failure of linearity by a factor 20 or so.

Their results are shown graphically in Figure 18. These are not the actual data but the model values fitted to the data using a maximum likelihood analysis. The values depend critically on the model assumed. Since in the absence of radon the risk to smokers and non-smokers is 25:1, by modelling the risk due to

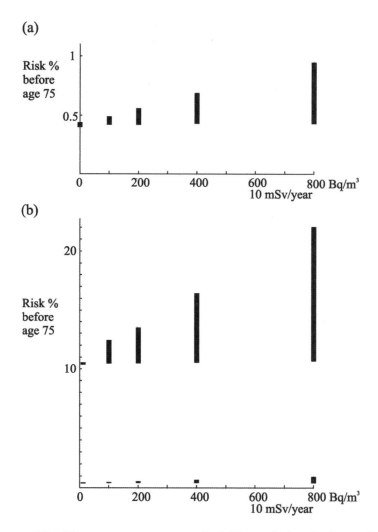

Figure 18   The percentage probability of death from lung cancer before age 75 shown for different values of the time-averaged radon environment: (a) plotted for non-smokers alone on a large scale; (b) for smokers (upper bars) compared with non-smokers (lower bars) together on a smaller scale. The data shown are the 90% confidence limits reported by Darby et al.

radon *relative* to its value at zero radon, the analysis of Darby et al assumes that the added radon risk is 25 times larger for smokers than for non-smokers. This use of multiplicative relative risk is not a linear assumption. Darby et al give no reason based on cell biology for this choice of non-linearity, but, evidently, smokers have a much larger sensitivity to the radon environment than non-smokers. The risks do not just add, and so superposition, the acid test of linearity, fails.

A conclusion for public health is that smoking alone is responsible for a risk of 10% of dying of lung cancer before age 75. The added stress on the various elements of the immune system of living in a high radon environment raise this figure to about 16%. However, the effect of radon for non-smokers is small – the risk of 0.1% or so should not be considered a serious concern, in the sense discussed on page 7. But, in any case, in a study of some 10,000 individuals statistical errors around 1% are to be expected, and consequently it is open to doubt whether there is any established risk due to radon for non-smokers. Indeed the error bars shown in Figure 18 are consistent with no dependence on radon at all, for smokers and for non-smokers.

At a practical level it is plain that, in the absence of smoking, the health risk from radon is so small that it cannot be demonstrated, even in a thorough Europe-wide study. It would therefore be better for public health if the extensive resources spent on reducing radon in homes and workplaces were spent, instead, on further measures to discourage smoking.

Radiation workers and dial painters

There are other groups who have experienced doses over long periods, such as radiologists, radiation workers and luminous dial painters. How do their health records compare with those of the general population? In fact, health varies significantly with socio-economic groupings, and so it is necessary to make the comparison with an appropriate mix who have not been exposed.

The mortality of UK radiologists has been compared with other professionals going back to the earliest treatments [37]. There is reported to be no effect for those registering since 1954, and before that date the observed effect is consistent with zero. The evidence is weak because the sample size (2,698) is too small and the doses are unknown.

An update on the health of UK radiation workers was published in 2009 by Muirhead [38]. Here the sample was much larger and the individual doses were assessed. The analysis was based on 174,541 workers employed by the Ministry of Defence, or government and related research industries. Their records have been followed to age 85 or January 2002, whichever was earliest. The average extra dose above natural background was 24.9 millisievert, accumulated over a number of years. This dose is very low but the number of workers is large so that statistical errors are small. The authors analysed the data to determine the standard mortality ratio, that is the number of deaths, divided by the number of deaths for a comparable population of workers, not exposed to radiation. So a real effect of ill health due to a history of radiation exposure would give a result in excess of 100%, within a range representing the statistical uncertainty. According to Muirhead [38] the mortality ratio for all cancers is between 81 and 84% after correction for social class effects. That is to say that radiation workers are healthier than their peers in other industries, from which the reader may conclude that it is healthy to work with radiation. The statistical uncertainty is small because the sample includes 26,731 deaths, so the conclusion should be rather clear. However, the authors choose to view the result as evidence that, although radiation is harmful, those who work with radiation are pre-disposed to be healthy, a so-called *healthy worker effect*. Once given a name and the acronym HWE, some view this interpretation as established. But others in the field [39] are not convinced. The reader may prefer the suggestion that a little radiation can be good for health.

A group of workers that experienced a large individually measurable dose over a long period are the painters of dials and clock faces. In the first half of the 20th century radioactive luminous paint was used to make the figures on these faces visible in the dark.[42] The people who were employed to paint these dials became contaminated, particularly because of a habit of licking the tip of the paintbrush to achieve fine detail. The alpha-emitting radium accumulated in bone, and, because this persists, it has been possible to assess individual doses accurately and retrospectively. The activity delivers a continuous whole-of-life dose, which is expected to induce a risk of bone cancer. In the general population only 1% of cancers is bone cancer and only one person in 400 is likely to contract it. As a result confounding effects are small. Data on the dial painters is given in a well known study by Rowland et al [40]. Out of 191 workers with whole-of-life doses greater than 10 gray, there were 46 cases of bone cancer (less than 1 expected). However, among 1,339 workers with accumulated dose of *less than* 10 gray, no cases of bone cancer were found (less than 3 expected). Unlike the non-smokers exposed to radon, or the radiation workers, this is unequivocal evidence for a damaging effect on health of a chronic lifelong dose. It is also not compatible with LNT and provides firm evidence for a threshold at about 10 gray for cancer due to a whole-of-life chronic dose. This is a most significant result.

Biological defence in depth

Radiobiology is part of the active field of research that has already confirmed the extraordinary level of protection that evolution has provided to cellular biology [41].

At the first level there is the production of anti-oxidants in cells, which may be stimulated by the occurrence of oxidative damage. Next there is the DNA repair mechanism for single strand breaks (SSBs), which is error-free and for double-strand breaks (DSBs), which may sometimes generate errors. Then there is cell death and apoptosis in which the whole cell is scrapped, including any DNA errors that it may contain. Finally there is the 'ethnic cleansing' effect of the immune system that kills cells that are not

---

[42] The atomic electrons of radioactive isotopes emit visible light following changes in the nuclear charge Z as a result of alpha or beta decay.

sensed to be 'one of ours'. This is the main defence against any viable mutation arising from a mis-corrected DSB. Radiobiologists now understand in outline how these mechanisms act together to protect life at the microscopic level from the major ravages of general oxidative attack, and also incidentally from the effects of irradiation. However, the report by BEIR [42] has objected that protection against radiation damage is quite distinct from that against oxidative attack. In fact the numbers that the report quotes seem at variance with its conclusion. It gives a Venn diagram [42, Fig. A1-1], the contents of which are summarised in Table 10.

Table 10   Comparison of the genes responsible for damage resistance in yeast from three studies, one of radiation and two of hydrogen peroxide [42]. The studies are compared in pairs. For each pair the overlap is the number of genes identified by both studies and the percentage is the overlap divided by the number identified by either.

Comparison of pairs of studies[43]	Number of genes in each	Overlap
Radiation with peroxide A	470 with 525	448 = 82%
Radiation with peroxide B	470 with 260	158 = 28%
Peroxide A with peroxide B	525 with 260	207 = 36%

This shows data from two studies of genes associated with oxidative damage due to hydrogen peroxide (a notoriously active chemical oxidant) and one study of genes associated with radiation damage. The mutual overlap of the two peroxide studies is 36% – presumably fair agreement, given that the methods were not identical. But, by the same measure, the 82% and 28% overlaps between the genes involved with radiation resistance and each of the peroxide oxidation studies are also in fair agreement. Independently of any details the evidence seems

---

[43] Data A and B from the studies of Game et al and Thorpe et al respectively.

to confirm that many of the same genes are involved in resisting radiative and chemical oxidative attack.

The various repair mechanisms may be stimulated by radiation and the extra adaptive protection afforded may persist for a certain time. An accessible account of current knowledge is given in the Report of the French National Academies [22]. Other recent studies include the report by the United Nations Scientific Committee on the Effects of Atomic Radiation [43]. There is extensive laboratory evidence for LNT failure and the adaptive response to radiation, as reported, for example, by Mitchel and Boreham [44]. They show that if cells are subjected to a continuous low dose over a period, mortality due to a subsequent single high dose is reduced. Corresponding effects are found in experiments with animals.

This beneficial effect, often called *hormetic*, is interesting, but to some extent it is a diversion from the main point. The observed hormetic effects are modest in scale, while the inappropriate level of current radiation safety requirements are much more pronounced. Hormesis strengthens the case, but is not essential to it. The fact that hormesis is not a large effect is to be expected because the various radiation defence mechanisms (anti-oxidants, DNA repairing and immunology) are stimulated already by normal oxidative attack, even in the absence of radiation. Radiation is a side show. Even among those who survived Hiroshima and Nagasaki and died of cancer, the number whose cancer was radiation-induced was a twentieth of those who died of cancer in the normal way, presumably initiated by oxidative attack.

The point is that the picture described by radiobiologists fits together, and the actual mechanism of the non-linearity is at least partially understood. No doubt further details will become clear, but the reason for the threshold is plain and the biological defence mechanisms are amazing in their ingenuity. This should be seen as really good news for mankind as he considers whether it is safe to exploit civil nuclear technology with greater enthusiasm.

Chapter 8 Nuclear Energy

Realising nuclear energy

In Chapter 3 we described how each nucleus remains at the centre of its atom, effectively without activity of any kind over aeons in time, aside from the slow gyration of its spin (if any) in passing magnetic fields and radiowaves, as occurs in MRI. But Figure 4 shows that in principle large amounts of energy could be released from nuclei, either through the fission of the heaviest or through the fusion of two of the lightest. Yet to a good approximation this does not happen at all, except in the extraordinary conditions at the centre of the Sun.

Some numbers on nuclear fission illustrate the point. Of all naturally occurring nuclei, only uranium-238 and uranium-235 undergo spontaneous fission. The half-life of uranium-238 is 4.5×10^9 years but the proportion that decays naturally by fission is only 5.4×10^{-7}. The numbers for uranium-235 are 0.7×10^9 years and 2.0×10^{-9}. So the fission rate for a uranium-238 nucleus is 8×10^{-17} per year, and for a uranium-235 the rate is 2×10^{-18} per year. These rates are exceptional – only one in a million uranium-238 nuclei has fissioned since the Earth was formed, and the rate for uranium-235 is even smaller. In fact natural (spontaneous) fission was only discovered in 1940, two years after neutron-induced fission was found by Hahn, Strassman and Meitner in Berlin. (Of course the conjunction of the date, December 1938, with the location was part of the drama to come.) But why are nuclei so reluctant to release their energy by fission?

The answer turns out to be closely related to the reason why the Sun has to be so hot at its centre to achieve fusion. The diagram in Figure 19a shows a nucleus, as a whole on the left and divided into two halves at progressively larger separations towards the right. The potential energy of the halves is the sum of the long-range electrical repulsion of their electric charge and the short-range nuclear attraction, both sketched in Figure 19b on different scales. The curves in Figure 19c and 19d show the net potential energy composed of these two effects added together, for the fusion of two light nuclei and the fission of one heavy nucleus, respectively. When the halves are in contact the nuclear force dominates, but if they are slightly separated they are too far apart

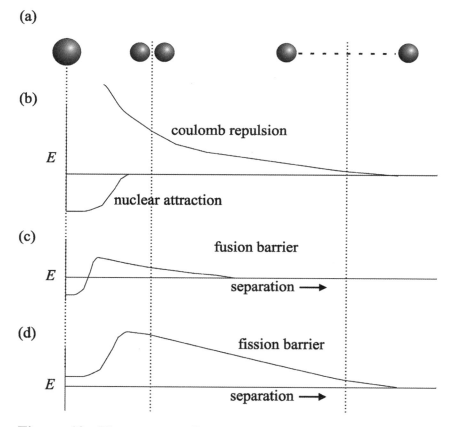

Figure 19 The energy of two halves of a nucleus, together (left), just separated (centre), and far apart (right). (a) Diagrams. (b) The two energy components, the repulsive and the attractive, not to scale. (c) The net energy sketched for the fusion of two light nuclei. (d) The net energy sketched for the fission of one heavy nucleus into two halves.

to feel anything except the disruptive influence of the electrical repulsion. As a result the energy curve forms a big 'hill', separating the condition of a single nucleus from that of two well separated halves. This hill is electrical in origin and is called the coulomb barrier, after Charles Coulomb, an 18th century pioneer in the field of electrostatics.

For fission to occur – for the two halves to separate – they have to have the lowest E when separated *and* be able to get over, or through, this barrier. The hill obstructs the change that delivers the energy.[44] Once through the barrier the two halves can slide down the remaining slope, rapidly gaining kinetic energy as they move further apart.

For fusion the problem is the other way around – the two smaller nuclei have to have the lowest E when together *and* be able to get inwards through the barrier, from right to left as shown. The curve for fusion is different in detail to the fission curve because the charges and distances are smaller. Only when they are very close together can the two halves feel the superior attraction of the nuclear force and slide down with the energy of the combined nucleus. To extract energy from fusion the barrier may be surmounted by extreme temperature and pressure, as happens in the Sun. The challenge of fusion power is to do this on Earth under controlled conditions for power generation. An important element of the nuclear story, looking to the future, is that fusion-based nuclear power stations are expected well within the next 50 years [45]. On the other hand schemes for fusion that circumvent the barrier by some 'cunning plan' or magical discovery are not expected to work.[45]

---

[44] Quantum mechanics helps. It is possible for particles to *tunnel* through the hill permitting slow leakage, otherwise the barrier would be even more effective. A similar effect permits slow alpha decay. Tunnelling rates depend exponentially on the height of the hill. Quantum tunnelling is also important in electronics.

[45] A well known recent 'breakthrough' called Cold Fusion professed to do this, but, predictably, its hopes have not been realised.

So viable rates of fusion occur when the components are heated to give them extra energy to get inwards through the barrier. But what about fission? How may energy be delivered to the components inside a uranium nucleus to help them get out over the barrier? The answer is by absorbing a neutron. Being electrically uncharged, a neutron can enter straight through the barrier and contribute its energy towards an excited nucleus, which then has the extra energy to fission rapidly over (or through) the barrier. Furthermore, in the fission process extra neutrons are produced and these can then go on to induce further fission, and so a chain reaction may ensue.

The first man-made nuclear fission reactor had to be based on uranium-235, because no other fissile material exists in nature.[46] Uranium-235 occurs naturally as 0.7% of natural uranium. This concentration of uranium-235, on its own in a reactor, does not sustain a chain reaction, because too many neutrons are lost from the chain through absorption by the majority uranium-238. To do this a neutron *moderator* is needed as part of the reactor, as explained later, or else the concentration of uranium-235 relative to uranium-238 must be enriched. The first man-made self-sustaining nuclear reactor was built by Enrico Fermi on the site of a racquets court at the University of Chicago in December 1942.

With the first reactor came a source of neutron flux, and with these neutrons it was possible to make fissile nuclear fuels other than uranium-235. Placed in such a uranium reactor, natural thorium-232 can capture an extra neutron to make thorium-233, which decays by beta emission to uranium-233. Similarly, plutonium-239 is made from uranium-238 by neutron absorption followed by two successive beta decays. Both plutonium-239 and uranium-233 are fissile fuels that can maintain a chain reaction. Plutonium was a totally new chemical element that was not found on Earth until made artificially in 1940.

---

[46] A fissile material is one that can sustain a nuclear fission chain reaction.

An important effect of the coulomb barrier is that it is very difficult to make materials radioactive. Aiming a source of ionising radiation at material does not have that effect, unless the energy is exceptional. Neutrons can do it because they get through the barrier, but beams of neutrons are not found in the environment because they are unstable and decay away in a few minutes. Electrons and gamma rays have little effect on nuclear structure, and protons and alpha particles are prevented from making other nuclei radioactive by the coulomb barrier. So, neutrons apart, the use of radiation does not make materials radioactive. This is a most important and reassuring aspect of radiation and nuclear safety. It needs to be appreciated when considering the use of processes like the irradiation of food or the sterilisation of hospital supplies.

Explosive devices

Although we are not really interested here in nuclear weapons and would rather avoid them, we need to appreciate how different their technology can be. In particular we need to understand why their fuel is different to that used in regular civil nuclear power stations.

A nuclear fission weapon relies on the rapid build-up of a neutron-induced chain reaction in high purity fissile fuel – that is uranium-235, plutonium-239 or uranium-233. Each nucleus of the fuel emits two or three further neutrons as it fissions. Each such neutron has a large chance to induce fission in a further nucleus, thereby releasing more neutrons and more energy. If the mass of fuel is small or dispersed, too many neutrons escape through the surface for this build-up to start – a condition described as sub-critical. For an explosion, two or more sub-critical masses have to be assembled to make a mass above the critical limit in which the build-up can then occur.

Timing is crucial, and the critical mass must be fully assembled before the chain reaction develops, otherwise the fuel blows itself apart before it has time to build up its full power. An efficient explosion should avoid a premature start, or *fizzle*, as it is known. This requires that the timescale of assembly be faster than the chain reaction build-up, and the mechanical dispersal be the slowest of all. This timing requirement limits the maximum size of a fission bomb – a larger one could not be assembled fast enough to avoid fizzle. The two methods of assembly that have been used are the gun barrel and the chemically driven implosion. With the gun method a sub-critical mass is fired into a hole in a second mass – this is effective with uranium-235. But for plutonium-239 it is too slow and the implosion method is required.

The chain reaction in a critical mass of fuel only begins when the first neutron appears. Where does this first neutron come from? If it comes from natural spontaneous fission its timing would be random, and, if this random rate is high, the chain reaction will start early, resulting in fizzle. Otherwise the start of the neutron build-up can be engineered with a *neutron initiator*, a neutron source made by mixing beryllium-9 with americium-241 at the critical time. Americium emits alpha radiation, and this reacts with the beryllium to give carbon-12 and the required neutron. This flux of neutrons gives the chain reaction a 'push start' just at the right time as the assembly comes together.

Table 11 Some fissionable isotopes with their fission fraction and fission rate per second for 1 kg.

Element-A	Half-life years	Spontaneous fission	
		Fraction	Rate per kg per second
uranium-233	2×10^5	1.6×10^{-12}	0.5
uranium-235	7.0×10^8	7×10^{-11}	0.06
uranium-238	4.5×10^9	5.4×10^{-7}	6
plutonium-239	2.4×10^4	4.4×10^{-12}	10
plutonium-240	6.6×10^3	5.0×10^{-8}	4.1×10^5
californium-252	2.6	0.03	2.3×10^{15}

So fuel for a nuclear weapon must have a high neutron-induced fission rate, but a low natural spontaneous rate. Table 11 gives spontaneous data for some isotopes of interest. With greater mass number A the spontaneous fission rate increases quite dramatically. So that any trace of californium-252, for instance, as an impurity in nuclear fuel would cause fizzle. Even plutonium-240 causes fizzle, unless its concentration is very low.

All of the isotopes listed in Table 11 can absorb a neutron to give an excited nucleus that then fissions. However, because the nuclear force gives an energy preference to neutrons that pair up in a nucleus (and likewise for protons), uranium-233, uranium-235 and plutonium-239 fission readily, even if the absorbed neutron has low energy. But that is not so for uranium-238 – upon absorbing a neutron it becomes uranium-239, which has an odd number of neutrons, and does not benefit from the neutron-pair premium. So it has less spare energy to overcome the coulomb barrier. As a result it usually emits a gamma ray rather than fission, unless the initial absorbed neutron is rather energetic. So uranium-238 is ruled out as a fissile fuel for weapons. However, it still has a large store of nuclear energy that can be used in civil power, and so also does thorium-232.

Uranium-233 is possible weapon fuel and it has been used in a test. However, in storage it builds up a concentration of uranium-232, which emits high energy gamma radiation. This makes it a hazardous choice as the basis of a weapons system – that is hazardous from a practicable handling and maintenance perspective.

That leaves plutonium-239 and uranium-235 as the preferred fuels for weapons. In each case weapons-grade fuel must be free of other isotopes. Uranium fuel should have more than 80% of uranium-235 to avoid neutron absorption by uranium-238; plutonium fuel should have less than 7% plutonium-240 to avoid fizzle on account of its high spontaneous fission rate. These requirements do not apply to fuel for civil power production, for which much lower purity is quite sufficient and fizzle is not relevant. The critical mass for uranium-235 is about 20 kg and for plutonium-239 about 6 kg.

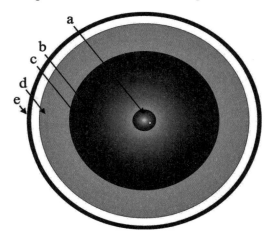

Figure 20 A diagram illustrating the relation between the components of a fission-based nuclear weapon:
a, neutron initiator;
b, fissile fuel;
c, tamper;
d, chemical explosive;
e, steel vessel.

A physical explosive device, fired by chemical implosion, has a number of concentric elements, illustrated symbolically in Figure 20. At the centre is the neutron initiator and around that the core of fissile fuel. Then comes the heavy *tamper* material with high atomic mass number that reflects neutrons back into the fuel to reduce surface losses. The chemical explosive develops implosion speeds as high as 5,000 to 7,000 metres per second to compress the fuel and the tamper inwards with a physical shock wave. The whole is encased in a steel containment vessel to reflect the initial compression wave inwards.

Enriching uranium-235 for weapons-grade fuel requires a large-scale high-technology industrial plant with an abundance of energy. Although there are a number of methods, none is easy because the two isotopes differ by only 1% in mass. In the early days the separation method used was mass spectrometry and later diffusion. The compound, uranium hexafluoride, is a gas at normal pressure and a temperature above 57°C. This makes it suitable for separation by diffusion. Being 1% lighter, the more nimble uranium-235 hexafluoride molecules are faster in the race through the diffusion tanks than those of the more ponderous uranium-238. But the difference is small and some 1400 diffusion stages are needed to reach 4% purity. For weapons-grade purity many more stages are required.

Today separation plants employ high speed centrifuges instead of diffusion. Such centrifuges were not available in the 1940s because materials technology was not developed to withstand the forces involved. Cylinders, 15–20 cm in diameter and rotating a thousand times a second, subject the uranium hexafluoride gas to an acceleration a million times gravity; this enriches the concentration of uranium-235 at the centre of the cylinder relative to the edge [46]. To make weapons-grade fuel requires many such stages, although far fewer are sufficient for civil reactor fuel. Such plant is more compact and less energy intensive than the earlier methods, and an important political question is how well it can be concealed from the eyes of neighbouring states and international inspectors.

The alternative to enriched uranium-235 is plutonium-239, also in rather pure form. This may be produced in a reactor by neutron absorption on uranium-238, followed by two successive spontaneous beta decays. However, the probability that this plutonium-239, once made in the reactor, captures a further neutron to make plutonium-240 is rather high – and plutonium-240 is a most undesirable contaminant for weapon-grade fuel because it causes fizzle. Consequently the uranium fuel (and with it the plutonium-239) has to be removed from the reactor rather frequently, before it has time to absorb the extra neutron. This is a most inefficient use of the reactor fuel – some 10 tonnes of uranium must be processed to extract a critical mass of plutonium-239. A nation state that tries to set up production of weapons-grade plutonium fuel using civil power reactors, which it claims to use for electricity generation, must spend much time shutting the reactors down for extra, and otherwise inexcusable, fuel changes. These fuel changes, and the construction of the required fuel reprocessing plant, make it obvious that plutonium fuel for weapons is being manufactured. At every reactor such activity is routinely monitored by international teams, as for weapons-grade uranium enrichment.

The first plutonium bomb was a test device called Trinity which was detonated on 16 July 1945 in the New Mexico Desert. Of the two bombs dropped on Japan on 6 August and 9 August 1945, one used plutonium and the other uranium. The result was that World War II ended on 15 August without the need for a land-based invasion of Japan.

There is a limit to the size of any nuclear fission weapon because of the difficulty of assembling a large critical mass within the time constraint – the fission bombs dropped on Japan were equivalent to 15 and 22 kilotonnes of TNT. Thermonuclear weapons based on fusion are not limited in size in this way and many were detonated in tests during the Cold War, although none has ever been used in anger. Just as a fission weapon is ignited by a chemically driven compression, the fuel for a fusion device is compressed and heated by an implosion driven by nuclear fission. This is necessary for the hydrogen to reach a sufficiently high temperature and density for long enough for the nuclei to overcome the coulomb barrier. This barrier is lowest when both nuclei have a single charge – that is hydrogen. Rather than simple hydrogen, its isotopes deuterium and tritium are used as fuel. The fusion products are helium-4 and a neutron. So the technology to build a fusion weapon requires fission as a trigger, and the feasibility of the two are closely linked.

A chemical explosion is quite distinct from a fire. In a fire the energy is released progressively over a period of time and this may be dangerous if not controlled, but an explosion is quite different, because the energy is released all at once to give a shockwave, a physical blast. Combustible materials and explosives are not the same. And so it is with nuclear energy too. The fuels can be distinct and the technology required for a civil nuclear power plant is different to that used in nuclear weapons, fission or fusion. Importantly, the design and operation of a nuclear reactor making fuel for weapons is different to a civil plant, used purely for the generation of electricity. The construction of reactors designed to produce fuel that can be used for weapons, the so-called breeder reactors, should form no part of a civil nuclear programme in the era of climate change.

Civil power from fission

During the Cold War period many fission power reactors were designed also to produce weapon-grade fuel, and this has left an unfortunate legacy in the public mind. But the history of nuclear reactor design is a story of problems on other levels too – materials, control engineering and corporate financing.

Over the last 50 years improvements in materials technology have benefited every aspect of life. We have come to expect, for example, failure-free plastics and long-lived structures that can operate under harsh conditions. The evolution of new technologies is often painful in the development stage but successful in the end. In recent decades the tools of finite element analysis, computer simulation and monitoring systems have increased the speed and assurance with which developments are made. A good example is the diesel engine – over the last 50 years its design has been transformed. The way in which nuclear power plants can be built for efficiency and reliability is no exception.

All technologies suffer financial quakes in the development phase. For example, the IT industry has been a succession of cycles of boom and bust, ever since the first attempts to lay and operate a transatlantic cable in the middle of the 19th century. However, no one could say that it has not delivered benefits to mankind. Similar oscillations of confidence have plagued the nuclear industry, although this was made worse by the political pressure that generated links between military and civil programmes. Today, such links are undesirable, unnecessary and relatively easily monitored. They are undesirable, not least because they connect the fear of nuclear weapons with civil nuclear power in the public mind, and this has become the major image problem for nuclear power.

(a)

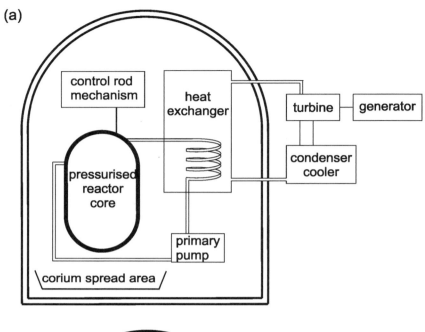

(b)

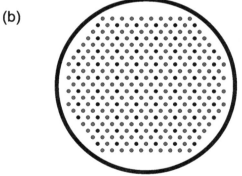

Figure 21   (a) The general features of a modern nuclear fission power reactor, in this case water cooled and moderated, and isolated in a double wall containment vessel. (b) A section across the pressurised reactor core vessel showing the matrix of fuel rods and neutron absorber control rods, immersed in the water as coolant and moderator. (This is a simplified sketch of the Areva EPR 1.6 GWe reactor where the pressurised core vessel is 12.7m in height [47].)

The really important safety features of a reactor are those that are responsible for the control and stability of energy production, and this depends on certain generic principles. If these fail, further safety systems ensure that the reactor contents are not released outside into the environment.

To understand the way in which a nuclear reactor works, it is instructive to follow how the energy flows, starting from the nucleus of the fuel and ending at the electric turbines that feed the power grid. First, a nucleus in a fuel rod within the reactor core absorbs a neutron and fissions, also emitting two or three neutrons which carry off the released nuclear energy. The fuel rods are surrounded by the moderator. This is made of low mass atoms, chosen to transform the released energy of the neutrons into heat. The neutrons bounce elastically off these low mass atoms, sharing their kinetic energy with them in the process. Then the material of the moderator transfers its acquired energy to the primary cooling circuit by thermal conduction or convection. A heat exchanger passes this energy onward to a secondary circuit that feeds the generating turbines. Exactly how these stages work varies with reactor design.

Figure 21a is a simplified drawing of the Areva Evolutionary Power Reactor (EPR) [47], chosen as an example of a modern design. In this case the moderator is water, which also acts as the coolant in the primary circuit. Figure 21b shows the reactor core with its matrix of fuel elements and neutron absorber rods that are inserted whenever the neutron flux is to be shutdown. Below the pressure vessel of the reactor core is the *corium spread area*, designed to retain the result of an overheated core within the double containment vessel, in the event that this should ever be necessary. The four-fold parallel safety control systems are omitted from the figure, but are described on the Areva website [47].

The nuclear fuel itself has to be replaced when 'spent'. How often this happens is determined by the structural integrity of the fuel elements and the build-up of fission products – the extent to which the fuel is fully used is called the *burn-up*, measured as a percentage or in megawatt-days per tonne. Typically fuel elements spend up to three years in the reactor core before replacement.

What properties should a good moderator have, and what other choices are there for the moderator and coolant, apart from water?

The chance of neutron-induced fission of uranium-235 or plutonium-239 is increased if the neutron energy is low. So, by lowering the neutron energy, the moderator improves the fission rate and reduces neutron absorption by uranium-238 at intermediate energies.[47] The effectiveness of its low mass atoms in slowing the energetic neutrons may be understood as follows. If two balls of equal mass collide, after the collision they will tend to share their energy equally on average, regardless of which ball had the most energy in the first place. On the other hand, if the energetic one is much lighter than the other, it simply bounces off the heavy one and there is not much sharing.[48] To maximise such energy sharing with neutrons, moderators with light atoms are chosen, such as graphite, water or heavy water.[49] An ideal moderator absorbs few neutrons, so that a chain reaction can be sustained without the need for enriched fuel. Ordinary water containing low mass hydrogen-1 is a good moderator and cheap. However, because of its neutron absorption, it requires fuel enriched up to 5%. The neutron flux is finely controlled by adding boron to the water which increases its absorption. Heavy water is not a strong absorber and does not

---

[47]   The problem has to be analysed carefully. The granularity of the fuel/moderator mix is important, as is the ability of the moderator to reduce the neutron energy in a small number of large steps, rather than a large number of small ones, which would increase the risk of absorption at the energy of many narrow resonances.

[48]   If neutrons hit electrons, the neutrons would be cooled very efficiently indeed. But because the neutron has no charge and the electron no strong nuclear force, such collisions do not occur.

[49]   In heavy water the isotope hydrogen-2, deuterium, is present in place of regular hydrogen-1. So heavy water is only 10% (20/18) denser than ordinary light water. Heavy water forms 0.015% of natural water.

require enriched fuel but it is not readily available. Graphite is not so efficient as a moderator and reactors that use it are larger. Furthermore, its crystal structure absorbs energy from the neutron bombardment. If not carefully managed, this energy[50] can be released unintentionally – this was the cause of the Windscale accident in 1957 [24].

The choice of coolant in the primary circuit depends on the core temperature and the requirement that it should not become too radioactive as it circulates through the core. Different designs use water, carbon dioxide or liquid sodium. The circulating coolant fluid has to transfer energy from the inside to the outside of the containment vessel, and the heat exchanger separates the coolant in the primary circuit from the secondary circuit that feeds the turbines. This improves the isolation of the latter from any possible radioactive contamination.

The objectives, against which any design may be assessed, are the efficient conversion of nuclear energy into electricity, the stable operation of the reactor, the containment of radioactive material, and the cost. Other factors that affect the total energy output and therefore the cost effectiveness are the refuelling cycle, the extent of maintenance shutdown periods and the working life of the reactor.

The highest efficiency at which heat can be converted into electric power is called the Carnot efficiency[51] and this depends on the absolute temperature of the thermal source. So a high working temperature of the cooling circuit is required if the conversion by the turbines is to be efficient. Although a high temperature improves efficiency, it also limits the choice of coolants and makes for a more hostile physical and chemical environment in the reactor. This affects the ageing and ease of maintenance of the reactor. The EPR design operates at a reactor pressure of 155 atmospheres and temperature of 310°C with an

---

[50] This is called the Wigner Energy.

[51] For an ideal thermodynamic engine this is given by $1-T_1/T_2$ where T_1 is the exhaust absolute temperature and T_2 is the input absolute temperature.

efficiency of 35%. The importance of operating at high temperature is evident because this efficiency is still only modest. Reactor power is quoted in GWt (gigawatts thermal) or, more often, GWe (gigawatts electric) – the ratio between these is the efficiency. This means that 65% of the total energy output is lost and is discarded as warm water to cooling towers or sea water – twice as much as the electrical energy generated. The large volumes of low-grade heat are not easy to use, but with good planning some of this surplus energy can be used to heat homes and greenhouses in the neighbourhood. The same consideration applies to fossil fuel plants. If power plants are preferentially sited far from centres of population, these options are reduced – and for political reasons this is usually the case for nuclear power plants. These are often built by the sea to take advantage of its large cooling capacity with some benefit to efficiency. The seawater is then also to hand as input to a possible linked desalination plant.

A reactor steadily delivering power needs a steady neutron flux in every part of its core. For this to be stable, each fission must produce just enough neutrons to go on to create exactly one further fission, on average. This depends on the neutron energy spectrum because that determines the balance between the rates of absorption and fission. Closely related are the temperature and density of the moderator. This raises two questions. The first is, how fast does the reactor respond to changes of absorber, for instance the position of the control rods?

In a nuclear weapon, mechanical speeds implemented by explosives are required to achieve the neutron flux change needed. Fortunately the neutron flux in a reactor behaves quite differently and responds rather slowly. This is because some fission neutrons come from the decay of short-lived neutron-rich fission products and their emission is therefore delayed. As a result, the reaction rate responds quite gently to small changes in the position of the control rods and slow mechanical feedback is sufficient.

The second question concerns stability. If the neutron flux rises a little so that the power output and the temperature increase, does the increased temperature reduce the neutron flux and re-establish equilibrium or increase the flux still further? Such temperature stability is an important requirement for any modern reactor design. For stable operation, as the temperature of the reactor increases, the neutron-induced fission rate should fall – without any intervention. This depends on the moderator and other details of the design. Early designs including that used at Chernobyl did not have this inherent stability.

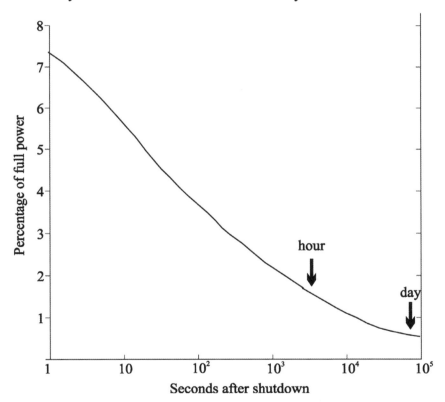

Figure 22   The decay of reactor power following shutdown (decay heat).

In the event of a power failure or other emergency, the neutron absorber rods should fall into place by default to cut the neutron flux and implement a shutdown, but cooling still has to be maintained. If the neutron flux is reduced to zero and the reactor is shut down completely, it continues to produce energy. This *decay heat* starts at 7% of the previous reactor output and decays away quickly and then more slowly, as it has contributions from many exponential radioactive decays, some with long half-lives. This fall-off is shown in Figure 22. After an hour the power drops to 2% and after a day to just over 0.5%. The consequence is that significant cooling continues to be needed following an emergency shutdown. In the EPR design this is provided by standby emergency diesel pumps backed up by extra water supplies fed by gravity. In the unlikely event that these fail and the core overheats, the reactor fuel must be contained even if the reactor pressure vessel fails. Provision is made for this extreme combination of eventualities in the form of a core spillage area within the containment vessel where hot radioactive core material (the *corium*) can cool without an environmental release of activity. More detail can be found on the Areva website [47].

Because of the release of decay heat it is difficult and inefficient to turn nuclear power plants on or off as electricity demand fluctuates. Such switching contributes to the ageing processes that eventually limit the working life of a reactor. This is why nuclear power is best used to provide the baseload supply, leaving more easily switched sources such as hydroelectric or gas plants to provide for fluctuations.

Energy without weapons

A chemical explosion is triggered by the excitation of molecules that are locked in an unstable state at normal temperatures. The excitation may be electrical or thermal, and the result of the explosion is a release of energy and gas, often nitrogen. One of the most famous such explosives, dynamite, was invented by Alfred Nobel in 1866. An obituary to him, erroneously published in 1888 while he was still alive, condemned him for this invention stating, *Le marchand de la mort est mort,*[52] and then continued,

> *Dr Alfred Nobel, who became rich by finding ways to kill more people faster than ever before, died yesterday.*

This is said to have brought about his decision to leave a better legacy on his death. All the great men who shared in the task of laying the foundations for nuclear technology partook of this legacy by winning the Nobel Prize.

The fuel for a simple fire based on chemical combustion is not the same as a chemical explosive. Fuels that burn are very common indeed, but fuels that explode are rather unusual. Similarly, the relatively simple fuel used for peaceful applications of nuclear technology cannot be used for nuclear explosives. So in both cases the fuels are different. In the nuclear case they require quite different levels of isotopic purity that cannot be confused unintentionally – they may be confused on purpose, of course, but that is a matter of deception and politics. The scientific signs of such deception are not easy to hide.

Uranium fuel for use in civil reactors designed simply to generate electric power needs either no enrichment in uranium-235, or an enrichment of 3–5%. Higher purity is not necessary. As for plutonium fuel, if the proportion of plutonium-240 is greater than 19%, the plutonium is termed reactor grade. Such fuels are quite safe to the extent that they cannot be used to make an effective nuclear explosion – that would require a concentration level of plutonium-240 of less than 7%. Purification of plutonium-239 by removing the plutonium-240 would be far more difficult, even than the enrichment of uranium-235 – the mass difference of the isotopes is only one part in 240, instead of three parts. Technically it would not make sense to attempt this on a practical scale.

A sub-critical mass of fuel still releases a small amount of radioactive energy in the form of alpha and beta radiation, so that it is warm, or hot in large masses if not cooled. Exceptionally,

---

[52] The merchant of death is dead.

some isotopes emit gamma radiation as well and the use of these is avoided because they are hazardous. Otherwise, if shielded by a modest thickness of absorber like a glove, unused fuel may be safe to handle. In the 1950s on a visit to Harwell Queen Elizabeth was handed a lump of pure plutonium-239 in a plastic bag and invited to feel its warmth.[53]

Depleted uranium is a substance that has caused much public concern [48] even though it is less hazardous than natural uranium. It is described as *depleted* because it is the spoil of the enrichment process. It is a useful material because it is a hard metal of exceptional density (19 times that of water). Typically it has less than half the activity of natural uranium. The alpha radiation that it emits is readily absorbed by a thin film of any material – it only forms a hazard to any extent if it is ingested. Like aluminium the bare metal is normally protected chemically by a hard natural oxide film – only in powder form is it chemically reactive. Like many other elements, for example copper, uranium would also be chemically toxic. But, because it is not absorbed by the body, copper is treated as an exceptionally safe material. With depleted uranium, it is lack of real information and confidence that is the problem. Armed forces using depleted uranium need to understand and be able to make judgements, otherwise they will not be confident with their weaponry.

The important task is to distinguish the military use of nuclear materials from their peaceful use. Compared with the production of other weapons of mass destruction, the manufacture of nuclear weapons remains difficult, and monitoring it is easier. Although the availability of civil nuclear power reactors for electricity generation is widely spread around the world, their misuse for the manufacture of weapons-grade plutonium fuel can be detected by monitoring reactor fuel changes, the choice of certain

---

[53] This is fact. A different story is emphasised in fiction. The script of the BBC TV film, *Edge of Darkness* (1985), has the principal character, Jedburgh, dying of radiation sickness following contact with plutonium.

reactor designs[54], and the use of fuel reprocessing plant. Large-scale multi-stage enrichment facilities for uranium are also monitored. These tasks are carried out at the international level by the International Atomic Energy Agency (IAEA).

Another indicator of nuclear weapon production is the development of certain technologies, such as high speed centrifuges and the neutron trigger. Prior to the First Iraq War it was noticed that Saddam Hussein was acquiring this neutron trigger technology.

Waste

The severity of any waste problem depends on how much waste is generated and where it is discharged. There are other equally important questions. On what timescale is the waste released? What kind of risk does it generate? For how long does it persist as an extra hazard in the environment once released?

In Table 12 these considerations are compared for typical coal-fired and nuclear-powered electricity generating stations. The differences between the various fossil fuels – coal, oil and gas – are small (the chemical energy per ton of carbon dioxide emitted is roughly in the ratio of 1:1.7:2.2 for coal:oil:gas). The lesser effect of sulphur is omitted from the table because this can be captured and neutralised with available technology.

The production of carbon dioxide by a coal-fired power station is prodigious. The combustion of each ton of carbon creates 3.6 tons of carbon dioxide, because it locks up the oxygen too. The facts are that a gigawatt fossil fuel power station discharges over six *million* tons of carbon dioxide into the atmosphere each year and that this carbon dioxide persists there for a century or so, on average, before being reabsorbed by vegetation, oceans and soil.

---

[54] For example, reactors moderated by heavy water can be refuelled without shutdown. But heavy water is not readily or cheaply available. It can be made by the electrolysis of large quantities of natural water, but this requires correspondingly large amounts of electric power whose use can be detected.

Table 12   A comparison of the typical waste products generated by a large power station using either fossil fuel or nuclear fission.

	Fossil fuel	Nuclear fission
Risk due to waste if released	Climate change	Cancer and other health hazards
Quantity of waste generated by 1 GW power station per year	6,500,000 tons carbon dioxide 22,000 tons nitrous oxide (coal) 320,000 tons of ash, incl 400 tons arsenic and toxic heavy metals	27 tons high level waste (5 tons when reprocessed and vitrified) 310 tons medium level waste 460 tons low level waste
Release into the environment	carbon dioxide, nitrous oxide, immediate atmospheric release ash and heavy metals, no early release but shallow burial	no early release, but deep burial after (high level) reprocessing and vitrification
Persistence in the environment if released	carbon dioxide, about 100 years nitrous oxide, about 100 years heavy metals, indefinite	iodine and xenon, a few weeks strontium and caesium, about 100 years actinides, indefinite

Less important are the large quantities of ash containing hazardous heavy metals. These are buried in shallow landfill sites where they persist indefinitely. The numbers in Table 12 are not precise – but it is the factors of ten, a hundred, a thousand and a million that are important. For instance, the fact that gas is only half as bad as coal is almost irrelevant.

The mass of carbon dioxide makes any scheme for its removal highly problematic. Even if pumped underground at high pressure, as has been suggested, it remains potentially a gas. Although out of sight if captured in this way, in reality it is stored in a pressure vessel at 50 atmospheres or more. In an earthquake or other accident such a geological container, with its pent-up internal pressure, could leak and vent its contents under pressure into the atmosphere as if it had never been stored.

The problem is described as *carbon capture*, but giving it a name does not mean that the large-scale technology is available at a realistic price. At best, it is a small component of the overall solution to the energy problem; at worst, it is an expensive idea, fraught with risk. There is already a very large charge of greenhouse gas stored in the sub-polar permafrost, and there is a significant concern that this may be released as these regions warm – storing further gases for the future seems undesirable, even if it were affordable. Buried solids such as ash or radioactive waste are quite different. They have no such hidden pressure and would not be released into the environment in the event of an earthquake.

Nuclear waste differs from fossil fuel waste in two essential ways – its quantity is small and it is not released. It is small because a nuclear power station needs only about a millionth as much fuel as a chemical power station for the same energy production (see footnote 6 on page 29). Then, unlike carbon dioxide, the waste from a nuclear power station can be stored, processed and then buried safely.

Broadly this spent nuclear fuel waste has three constituents.

1. There are the actinides, comprising the unburnt fuel and various radioisotopes generated from it – essentially that part of the fuel that has not fissioned. The isotopes, including plutonium and uranium itself, may be extracted chemically by reprocessing and re-used for fuel, and as such they are very valuable. Exceptionally, if they are dispersed into the environment in a major accident, as at Chernobyl, they do not melt or vaporise and are not thrown far into the atmosphere. However, many have extremely long half-lives and so persist – although not for as long as the toxic heavy metal waste from a coal-fired plant, such as arsenic and cadmium, the power of whose chemical toxicity never diminishes at all.

2. Then there are the products of the fission itself. As the process of fission suggests, these have atomic masses that are about half of that of uranium. Many decay quite quickly to more stable isotopes. The faster decay processes are the source of the decay heat that follows the chain reaction (Figure 22). Of most concern are those with longer half-lives, in particular strontium-90 and caesium-137 with half-lives of about 30 years. So after the initial rapid decline, the activity of fission products falls by a factor two every 30 years.

3. Finally there are a few volatile products of nuclear fission with shorter half-lives. Examples are iodine-131 and xenon-133 with half-lives of a week or so. These decay away completely in a few months. Some are vented into the atmosphere in harmless quantities but others are removed by filtering and the filters buried as low level waste. Other fission products are less significant, either because they are less volatile or because they have short half-lives.

More generally, radioactive materials are managed with one of four strategies: 1, reprocess and re-use;   2, concentrate and contain; 3, dilute and disperse; 4, delay and decay.

Low level waste comes largely from laboratories, hospitals and industry. It consists of conventional garbage, tools, clothing and filters, contaminated by small quantities of mostly short-lived isotopes. It is not dangerous to handle and is safely disposed of by diluting and burying in relatively shallow sites [49]. It may be that with a more relaxed attitude to radiation some of this waste will not be seen to require disposal separate from other forms of waste. Such decisions will reduce costs.

Intermediate level waste includes resins, chemical sludges and reactor components, as well as contaminated materials from decommissioning. It makes up 7% of the volume, and 4% of the activity, of all radioactive waste. It may be solidified in concrete or bitumen. Generally short-lived waste from reactors is buried, but longer-lived waste from reprocessing is concentrated ready for later burial deeper underground [49].

In the event of the accidental dispersal of fission products, as happened at Chernobyl, land contaminated by caesium-137 is treated with regular potassium fertiliser to reduce its uptake into the food chain by dilution – caesium has a similar chemistry to potassium. In the same way, lime is used to dilute the effect of strontium-90 – calcium and strontium are chemically similar. Generally the dilution and dispersal strategy is not applied to high concentrations of these isotopes.

Spent fuel elements and their support cladding are the most radioactive types of waste. They are handled with strategies 4, 1 and 2, in succession. When the elements are withdrawn from the reactor, or it is shut down, the decay of neutron-rich fission-product nuclei continues and significant power is still released. Such materials are cooled for about 5 years by keeping them separated in large tanks of water, which also absorbs the emitted radiation in complete safety.[55] The materials may then be reprocessed to extract the actinides which can be recycled to make new fuel elements, such as MOX, composed of mixed oxides of uranium and plutonium. Of course the fraction of the spent fuel that has not fissioned and so can be recycled depends on the burn-up. In modern reactors the burn-up is still low but this could become higher in the future.

Having already given up their fission energy, fission products cannot be recycled. Their activity falls rapidly in the first 10 years. After that the radioactivity is largely due to strontium-90 and caesium-137, which decay with a 30-year half-life. So their activity drops by a factor of 10 after 100 years and 1,000 after 300 years. Long before that, after reprocessing these products can be chemically encapsulated by vitrification. The resulting ceramic blocks are extremely strong and resistant to leaching by ground water, or other mechanical or chemical attack. They are stored for 30–50 years above ground while they are naturally air-cooled, and then will be placed underground in a suitable deep mine or depository where they will maintain their integrity long after their radioactivity has faded away. In a few hundred years the radioactivity of the waste will drop to a level that can be found elsewhere in the Earth's crust. The reprocessing and vitrification of waste in this way is a mature technology that has an accident-free record of several decades. Only now is the earliest high level nuclear waste ready for disposal in a deep underground depository.[56]

An underground site for the long-term deposit of waste needs to be constructed, but this is not difficult or critical – not critical

---

[55] For example, the entire stock of used fuel from 15 years of operation of the Sizewell B power station is safely stored in a single tank that is less than half full.

[56] In some cases extra expense is involved in the disposal of the earliest 'legacy' waste, for instance the fuel rods from the Windscale fire of 1957. However, this work is now in hand. Benefiting from 50 years of experience, the disposal of waste from the plants of today will not incur such exceptional costs.

because the long-lived activity should have been removed by reprocessing. Radiation due to the vitrified fission products is a modest and contained hazard that requires security for a time that may be long in everyday terms, but is very short compared with the life of the blocks. Nevertheless, massive provision is being made for waste in some countries. In Finland a deep depository is under construction. A 5 m wide and 6.5 m high tunnel follows a helical path down to a depth of 500 m within structurally sound rock. Copper canisters containing nuclear waste will be placed in horizontal shafts that will be filled and sealed with clay. Use of the depository is expected to start in about 2020.

In the USA a depository at Yucca mountain in Nevada is due to receive its first nuclear waste by 2017. Matched to current safety regulations, such facilities may be thought overspecified. Such extraordinary precautions are not required and the expense could be reduced. The scale of these resources is primarily aimed at reassuring public opinion, rather than the provision of necessary safety. Such priorities cannot be afforded, and, in any case, it would seem that they are not effective at providing this reassurance. [Note added in proof, May 2009: It is reported that the US may discontinue the Yucca project and, perhaps, may recycle spent fuel, which has not been US policy in the recent past because of its association with weapons-grade plutonium production.]

In addition, there remains the need for public education. Also important is the need for technical continuity of know-how and recorded data. Inventories of radioactive materials and where they are stored, need to be maintained. Such records tend to have a short life compared with the physical and chemical integrity of any deposit. This short life is of most concern in countries where political stability is uncertain and social responsibility is short term. In any case depositories should be deep enough and burial irreversible, so that it matters somewhat less if records are lost during the few hundred years needed for the activity of the reprocessed waste to die away.

Chapter 9 Radiation and Society

History is a race between education and catastrophe.

H G Wells, writer (1866–1946)

Perceiving radiation

Why do people react as they do to questions of radiation? Many are ill at ease, not just because they do not know anything about it, but because they get no sensation when they are exposed to it. Many other hazards to life can be seen or felt in some way. A sensation of pain makes one alert to a danger, so that it is then easier to react and avoid it. Any agent that can harm, unseen and possibly without warning, encourages alarm and unrestrained flights of imagination.

A solution is to provide the missing personal verification – ensuring that individuals, alone or in groups, can see the danger or check its absence. In fact, at two separate levels we are able to sense radiation. Subconsciously, the cells in the body sense damage caused by radiation and initiate its repair. In addition, at a conscious level we can detect radiation with instruments. Such instruments may be seen as extensions of our senses. They are not different in principle from the biologically based lenses and light detectors that form our eyes, or pressure sensors that give us information through touch and feel. Much of the recent spectacular progress in medical physics can be understood as extending our ability to *see* using such instruments [4].

Provision of an ability for scientists and other authorities to see radiation is not a solution to the problem – in principle, *everybody* needs to be able to see. Confidence with radiation would be developed by making simple instruments cheaply available, just as torches or candles are easily obtained so that people are not frightened in the dark. This could start with education in school. Then, just as children play with a magnifying glass, and then progress to binoculars, microscopes and telescopes, they would become familiar with radiation detectors. With modern electronics such detectors can be made the size of a credit card, and it would be straightforward to add a basic detector as an option in a GPS device or digital camera. If industry were shown a market, this would happen quickly and cheaply. Admittedly children would quickly find that radiation levels are extraordinarily low, even rather uninteresting. But they would at least actually see that, and then go home with a reassuring message for their parents and friends – and there is no more effective way into the home than through the beliefs of children. Additionally they could be told what to do if their counter gave a high reading, instead of remaining quite ignorant as was the case for several days for those who lived near Chernobyl. Such civil defence procedures would be a small price to pay for a vigilant control of the environment.

Although modern miniaturised versions are fine, the least helpful kind of instrument is the classic geiger counter that emits a loud click for each quantum of radiation detected. The apprehension that can be created in an audience by an ever increasing rate – *click, click-click, click-click-click* – from such a counter is worthy of the soundtrack of the film *JAWS*! It is difficult to think of a less appropriate way in which to reassure people. In reality a single click is far too small to matter. The need is for simple digital measurements showing total accumulated radiation dose, and also dose rate – but no more clicks! These measurements would show gamma radiation and have some sensitivity to beta, and would usually be quite sufficient to indicate whether there was radiation in the environment.

Radiation is generally easy to measure, and it is not hard to record every atom as its nucleus decays by counting each quantum of ionising radiation as it reaches a detector. This is in spite of the fact that the corresponding risk of damage may be quite insignificant unless millions of counts are detected in this way. For example, one count might represent 1 MeV of energy. Although this is a lot of energy to a single biological molecule, the threshold of risk, a dose of 100 millisievert, corresponds to about a million such counts, depending on the efficiency and sensitive mass of the counter.[57] It is therefore rather easy to measure radiation clicks at levels where the danger is completely insignificant. In other words, the radiation level indicated by one click – or even many thousands of clicks – given by a radiation counter may be unimportant. This has confused public discussion of safe radiation levels. If the detection of radiation had been more difficult, the public perception might have been better matched to the true scale of the danger.

Public concern

The first time that the world at large learnt of radiation and the power of the nucleus was in August 1945. Since 1940 the physics and technology of nuclear weapons had been being developed by the USA in total secrecy. The work, in collaboration with British and Canadian scientists, was code-named the *Manhattan Project*. Few people knew about it until they read in the newspaper or heard on the radio about the dropping of the two bombs. The first reports in the press were brief.

> *Japan has been hit with an atomic bomb 2,000 times more powerful than the ten-tonners dropped by the R.A.F. on Germany. President Truman, disclosing its use today, said that even more powerful bombs are in development. British and American scientists have been working on it for years out of reach of German long-range weapons.*

The Manchester Guardian, 7 Aug 1945.

By 1945 the general population of the allied countries had become accustomed to the secrecy and propaganda that are

---

[57] If the sensitive mass of the counter is 1 milligram, then 100 millisievert represents 10^{-7} joules of energy in the counter mass. The number of clicks corresponding to 100 millisievert is therefore 10^{-7} joules divided by the energy per click, 1.6×10^{-13} joules – that is about a million.

necessary in times of war – trusting the state was the only option. The atomic bomb[58] was welcome news, a wonderful weapon to end the war with Japan quickly. With this sentiment came a vacuum in understanding that manifested itself as a sense that nuclear physics was not a subject that normal people could, or should, attempt to understand. Its comprehension was *not for the likes of me*. Unfortunately for many this perception still persists. The feeling of awe that is inspired by powerful physical processes affects everybody in society, scientists included. Indeed, often scientists are the most affected, as they appreciate the scales involved. So in 1945 they too were overcome by the size, the enormity even, of what had been achieved, and reacted in different ways when they came to reflect as human beings. Many were men of conscience who worried about the effect of nuclear weapons in a politically unstable world. They were not politicians or in the military, and felt responsible that they had delivered this power into hands that they did not altogether trust, and certainly could not control.

With the coming of peace people asked many technical questions. Few had the scientific background to follow the answers far, and certain sketchy ideas, some irrelevant, some true only in part, became current on the street and in the press – Einstein and his strange hairstyle, the meaning of $E = mc^2$, and the idea of a runaway nuclear chain reaction. These snippets may have impressed but did little to bring understanding and reassurance.

Testing and fallout

The decades of the Cold War brought no enlightenment. To worries about the explosive power of nuclear weapons were added separate concerns about radiation and its effects in the event of nuclear war – that is nuclear contamination, radiation-induced cancer and genetic change. It was understood that

---

[58] It is not clear how it collected the description *atomic* – it should be *nuclear*. This unfortunate error seems to have occurred, and been tolerated, from an early stage in the non-scientific description of the Manhattan Project.

nuclear fallout and its consequences would affect global regions, persist for a long time because of the half-lives concerned, and genetically influence future generations. For a long time the scientific data and understanding needed to give firm answers to these concerns were not available. In any case, the circulation of such concerns added to the fear that was essential to the Cold War strategy abroad. In the meantime, highly conservative regulations and radiation safety regimes were set up in an unsuccessful attempt to stem public fear at home.

The explosion of a nuclear weapon generates a blast that causes physical destruction by force, a direct flux of heat, neutrons and X-rays, and a consequential fire. The blast and firestorm have their counterpart in the impact of a conventional chemical explosive. The direct radiation flux of a nuclear detonation is intense but localised. The nuclear fallout comes from both the material of the bomb itself and the irradiated matter close by. The latter is increased if the detonation takes place at ground level rather than high in the atmosphere. As a result of the heat released, much material is sucked upwards as a column into the upper atmosphere. This material is particularly radioactive and returns to Earth slowly in hours, days or longer, according to its density, volatility and the pattern of wind and rain. This is the radioactive fallout.

Atmospheric testing of nuclear weapons started with the Trinity bomb of 1945 and ended essentially in 1963. The nuclear powers, primarily the USA and USSR, and later the UK, France and China, engaged in this testing, first fission weapons but then mainly thermonuclear devices. Atmospheric testing was discontinued by treaty, and later tests were carried out underground without contributing any fallout. The extent of these tests is summarised in Table 13.

During this period the fallout from atmospheric tests, equivalent to 20,000 times the energy of the Hiroshima bomb, contributed a worldwide radiation exposure that persisted for some years, as shown in Figure 23. This shows the long term contribution diminishing steadily after 1963. The small blip in 1986 is the modest effect of Chernobyl, as detected in the UK.

Table 13   The total number of nuclear weapon tests was about 2,080. The total power was about 500 megaton (a megaton is equivalent to a million tons of TNT).

	Atmospheric tests		Underground tests	
	number	megaton	number	megaton
USA	216	141	838	38
USSR	217	247	498	38
UK	21	8	28	1
France	136	10	68	4
China	23	22	21	1

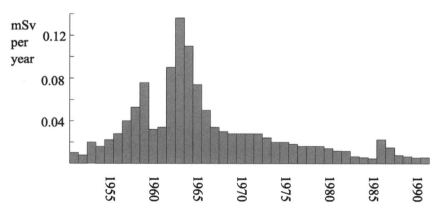

Figure 23   The contribution of radioactive fallout to the average annual radiation dose of the population of the UK during the years of nuclear testing and the Chernobyl accident [5].

The most significant radioactive components of nuclear fallout (with their half-lives) are iodine-131 (8 days), zirconium-95 (64 days), strontium-90 (29 years) and caesium-137 (30 years). The total release of strontium-90 in all these atmospheric tests was 75 times the release from Chernobyl – for caesium-137 the factor was 30 times.

The radiation dose from this fallout gave a global exposure of 0.15 millisievert per year at its peak in 1963. This was less than 4% of natural background – about equal to the extra radiation dose received from an annual holiday lasting a single week in Cornwall, UK. Figure 23 shows that the average UK dose due to Chernobyl was almost 10 times smaller again – at 0.002 millisievert per month, it would be at the bottom of Figure 17.

During the Cold War, the fear of nuclear weapons was driven by the thought of the fallout that would result from the detonation of *thousands* of nuclear weapons. The likelihood of such irrational behaviour by political and military leaders may seem rather small, but, given the number of warheads ready stockpiled at the time, it did not seem to be so then. A famous post-apocalyptic novel of the period, *On the Beach* (1957) by Neville Shute, described life on Earth after such an all-out nuclear exchange. Its popularity reinforced the standard stereotype view of radiation.

Nuclear tests in the atmosphere were carried out in very isolated places – the Nevada Desert, isolated Pacific islands or deserted regions in Kazakhstan. However, occasionally groups of people were caught within close range by mistake and suffered high radiation exposures from the fallout. For instance, in 1954 a low level thermonuclear test of 15 megatons exposed 23 Japanese fishermen in their boat, the *Fukuru Maru*, at a distance of 130 km to large doses in the range 2,000–6,000 millisievert. They became nauseous and suffered beta-decay-induced skin burns. One died within 6 months but most were reported to be still alive 30 years later.

Deterrence and reassurance

The deterrent effect of large stocks of nuclear weapons, deliverable at short notice, was essential to the Cold War. In part, the threat was the major destruction of cities and infrastructure at all levels, but also it was the more illusive prospect of widespread and lingering death by radiation – to be followed by genetic damage to later generations. Warfare has always involved such an unresolved mix of real and apparent threats. The pageantry of a mediaeval army, the splendour of a fleet of men-of-war with guns, sails and flags – these were all a mix of bark and bite. The separation of the two tested the confidence, sophistication and nerve of opposing forces.

An undesirable consequence of striking fear into the heart of the enemy is that those on the allied side become frightened also. And so it was in the Cold War. The whole population felt involved and shared in the fear of imminent destruction – and with it the threat of fallout and irradiation.

Sections of the population reacted by forming anti-war groups, such as the UK Campaign for Nuclear Disarmament (CND). In their advocacy, they aimed to win others to their cause by talking up the possible consequences of nuclear war, with special emphasis on radiation. In so doing they amplified the fear and alarm yet further.

Governments for their part sought to restrain and contain the level of domestic concern. In their attempts to reassure, they empowered committees to advise on radiation safety and propose limits which then became the basis for legislation. Foremost is the International Commission for Radiological Protection (ICRP). Its remit is to provide

> *recommendations and guidance on protection against the risks associated with ionising radiation, from artificial sources widely used in medicine, general industry and nuclear enterprises, and from naturally occurring sources.*

Other international committees were set up with remits that often overlapped: the Nuclear Energy Agency of the Organisation for Economic Co-operation and Development (OECD/NEA); the United Nations Scientific Committee on the Effects of Atomic Radiation (UNSCEAR). In addition there are national bodies, such as the Biological Effects of Ionizing Radiation (BEIR) committee of the US National Academy of Sciences, and the UK National Radiological Protection Board (NRPB), now subsumed into the Health Protection Agency (HPA). Then there is the International Commission on Radiation Units and Measurements (ICRU) with responsibility for questions of measurement. The World Health Organization (WHO) with its wider responsibilities also plays a central role.

These committees between them constitute a formidable safety group, largely beyond the control of any state or states. Half a century later their work continues, and, although the problem has changed, their remit has not.

One such body is rather different. The International Atomic Energy Agency (IAEA) has a distinct role as the world arbiter of the separation of the civil and military uses of nuclear technology. Its objective is to

> *seek to accelerate and enlarge the contribution of atomic energy to peace, health and prosperity throughout the world. It shall ensure, so far as it is able, that assistance provided by it or at its request or under its supervision or control is not used in such a way as to further any military purpose.*

This task has not changed and this UN agency has a role in the modern world, at least as important as it ever was [47].

Generally, these committees between them have collated the best available data and many of the documents referenced in this book were published by them. Health and safety recommendations based on this evidence are drawn up by ICRP, most recently in 2007. However, their summaries and conclusions address the remit of an earlier age, namely to advise on the reduction of radiation risks to a minimum, regardless of other non-nuclear consequences. ICRP was established to do that and so it could hardly be otherwise. The Commission is not in a position to consider broader matters, such as the impact of its recommendations on the environment. In the meantime, within the narrow field and with the benefit of half a century of effort, it has worked to make radiation regulation very safe indeed. It has done well – it has successfully carried out what it was asked to do, and its recommendations have become entrenched in national regulations, working practices and laws. Implementing these involves high costs that may be seen now to be more than the modern world can afford, either financially or in terms of other balancing dangers.

At the very least, this exceptional safety regime should have produced the benefit of public confidence in the use of radiation and civil nuclear power, but unfortunately it has failed to do even that. The mistake has been to try to achieve safety, primarily through blind obedience to restrictive instruction, rather than through cooperation and understanding based on enlightened education.

Judging radiation safety

So looking forward, as teachers, what should we tell our students about the dangers of radiation and radioactive contamination? And as parents, what should we say to our children? Generally, what should we tell the wider public?

A recent joint report of the French National Academies of Science and Medicine reviewed the whole field of the effect of low-dose radiation. This was published in 2006 [22]. An earlier edition was published in 2004/5 [21]. The abstract sets out the position on LNT and the basis of the Report's disagreement with ICRP.

> ... *This conclusion against the validity of LNT is based on several types of data:*
>
> *1. Epidemiology has not evidenced cancer excess in humans for doses below 100 millisievert.*

2. Experimental animal data have not evidenced a carcinogenic effect for doses below 100 millisievert. Moreover, dose-effect relationships are very seldom linear; most of them are linear-quadratic or quadratic. A practical threshold or hormetic effects have been observed in a large number of experimental studies.

3. Radiobiology: LNT assumes that the genotoxic risk (per unit dose) is constant irrespective of dose and dose rate and thus that the efficacy of the two guardians of the genome, DNA repair and elimination by death of cells with DNA damage do not vary with dose and dose rate. This assumption is not consistent with a large number of recent radiobiological data, for example mutational effect and lethal effect vary (per unit dose).

The second assumption is that a given DNA damage has the same probability of initiating a cancer irrespective of the number of other DNA damage in the same cell and in the neighbouring cells. This assumption is also non consistent with recent data and modern concepts of carcinogenesis in which the microenvironment and tissue disorganisation play an important role. The existence of a threshold dose in individuals or animals contaminated by radium or thorium shows that the irradiation of a cell surrounded by non-irradiated cells does not initiate carcinogenesis. It is the responsibility of the proponents of LNT to demonstrate the validity of these two assumptions in order to justify the use of LNT. The recent reports do not provide such demonstrations.

In essence this is the same message as that expressed in these chapters, but written in more academic language.

The concluding words of the 2004/5 edition of the Report are addressed to a wider audience [21],

Decision makers confronted with problems of radioactive waste or risk of contamination, should re-examine the methodology used for the evaluation of risks associated with very low doses and with doses delivered at a very

> *low dose rate. This report confirms the inappropriateness of the collective dose concept to evaluate population irradiation risks.*

Other radiobiologists have been more forthright. For example, in a recent article Pollycove and Feinendegen [41] point out the incompatibility of current knowledge and the whole edifice of the world radiation safety organisation,

> *Acceptance of current radiobiology would invalidate long established recommendations and regulations of worldwide radiation safety organizations and so destroy the basis of the very expensive existing system of regulation and remediation.*

Progress towards an internationally endorsed change of view has been slow, perhaps because ICRP, amongst others, seeks a different level of safety. The point is not a scientific one. It is this: is it right to pursue radiation safety to a level that is so low that, as a result, much larger risks are incurred elsewhere? In a widely accepted view, in the case of climate change, this larger risk is one with a chance of major global disaster approaching 100%.

The latest recommendations of the International Commission for Radiological Protection, ICRP103 [27], offer some major relaxations in estimated radiation risk, relative to the view taken in its 1990 Report. But this 2007 Report still clings to the language of LNT, although when pressed it concedes that this does not represent a belief in a linear mechanism so much as a way in which to parametrise the data. An example of its half-hearted adherence to LNT was referred to earlier on page 103. The Report is equally ambivalent when summarising its position on the existence of a damage threshold [27, p.210],

> *Although the available data do not exclude the existence of a universal low-dose threshold, the evidence as a whole ... does not favour this proposition.*

It goes on to comment on the contrary view,

> *(A) recent low-dose report from the French Academies ... emphasises evidence on the potential dose-dependence of post-irradiation cellular signalling, DNA repair, apoptosis and other adaptive anti-tumorigenic processes in order to argue for the existence of a practical low-dose threshold for radiation cancer risk. Overall, the long standing question on the true validity of the LNT model may well prove to be beyond definitive scientific resolution and that 'weight of evidence' arguments and practical judgements are likely to continue to apply in the foreseeable future.*

Such disdain by ICRP for meaningful scientific discussion of radiation safety suggests that they have now exhausted their lines of argument.

Elsewhere the ICRP Report acknowledges the existence of a threshold for high doses, and also for some conditions at low dose [27, p.143–144],

> *The dose responses for in utero radiation-induced tissue reactions, malformations and neurological effects are judged to show dose thresholds above a few tens of millisievert.*

But generally the Report continues to express risk in linear terms, for example by stating sensitivity as a coefficient of risk per unit dose. Expressed in this way, an assumption of linearity is implicit in all its recommendations. These ICRP linear risk coefficients for cancer and genetic effects have been used in Table 14 to show *absolute* risk, as chance per 1,000 at 100 millisievert. The cancer figure may be compared with the data shown in Table 5 (page 91). Note that the estimated heritable or genetic risks are eight times smaller than the value recommended in 1990 and 30–40 times smaller than the cancer risks. This is a major change for ICRP to make, and it indicates that even the most cautious views are changing, if slowly. It is reassuring that it is universally accepted on the basis of evidence that dangers due to radiation-induced mutations are small, and that this concern can be played down.

Table 14   ICRP risk coefficients for cancer and genetic effects, re-expressed as chance per 1,000 for 100 millisievert [27, Table 1, p.53].

	Cancer		Heritable effects	
	2007 values	1990 values	2007 values	1990 values
Whole population	5.5	6.0	0.2	1.3
Adults only	4.1	4.8	0.1	0.8

The cancer risk given by ICRP, as expressed in Table 14, has not been changed significantly since 1990. At 100 millisievert the numbers are consistent with the data shown in Table 5. However, there are differing views about risks at low acute doses, which may be summarised as follows [50].

- The optimists (the French National Academies [21, 22], Pollycove and Feinendegen [41], among many radiobiologists) say that the data are consistent with no risk below 100 millisievert.
- The pessimists (ICRP, BEIR and others) say that the risks are consistent with LNT.
- Both views are compatible with the data for a single acute dose, for instance the health records of the Hiroshima and Nagasaki survivors.
- The optimists explain the mechanism involved while the pessimists adhere to their unexplained linear faith.

The conclusion might be drawn that it does not matter whether you follow the optimists or the pessimists, and, to an extent, that is correct for a single acute dose. The risk below 100 millisievert is so small that it cannot be measured, even on the basis of a 50-

year international study of the consequences of dropping two nuclear bombs on the inhabitants of two large cities. So the conclusion of the optimists is not really an issue, and an acute exposure of 100 millisievert is safe.

The difference between the position taken by the optimists and the pessimists comes in the effect of repeated doses, real or hypothetical. The pessimists, because of their adherence to LNT, consider that each dose, even below 100 millisievert, adds to the lifetime dose of the individual as an invisible creeping inventory of accumulated radiation exposure – and that dose leaves an indelible mark on health. The optimists point out that this is quite incompatible, both with data on multiple and chronic doses, and with a basic picture of modern radiobiology.

It is a separate but no less important concern that the pessimists' view makes the use of nuclear technology very expensive and deters its use in the reaction to escalating climate change. These views are not just a matter for academic debate. Society at large has a serious interest, but, although the publications are not secret, few outsiders are sufficiently aware of the issues.

Chapter 10 Action for Survival

The policy of being too cautious is the greatest risk of all.

Pandit Nehru, Prime Minister of India (1889–1964)

Relaxed regulations

Generally, in the early years of a fresh technology when less is understood, safety regulations should be restrictive in order to cover for the unknown to some extent. Then, as knowledge improves and the science becomes better understood, acceptable limits can be relaxed responsibly and with a clear conscience. With the relaxation can come greater levels of technical exploitation, and then improved prosperity and confidence. Unfortunately, this is not what often happens. The enactment of regulation is clumsy and often painfully slow, following disaster rather than preceding or preventing it. Then later, in a mistaken quest for absolute safety, legally inspired caution is used to generate ever tighter restriction under an ill-advised banner such as *you cannot be too safe*. Unfortunately, as knowledge builds, regulation is not rolled back as it should be, but often continues to tighten under the pressure of out-of-date information or the corporate tunnel vision of one or more pressure groups.

In the matter of radiation safety, in 60 years the regulation has tightened and the understanding has improved significantly such that the two are now far apart. In 1951 a limit was set by ICRP at 3 millisievert per *week* [27, p.35]. In 1957 this was tightened to 5 millisievert per *year* for the public and 50 millisievert for radiation workers. In 1990 these annual limits were reduced further to 1 millisievert and 20 millisievert, respectively. The limit for the public is 150 times tighter than in 1951. In addition, from 1955 the advice was given that

> *every effort should be made to reduce exposures to all types of ionising radiation to the lowest possible level.*

Various changes in the wording were made before this principle gained the acronym, ALARA, *as low as reasonably achievable*. Over the years, under public pressure and with improved measurement and other technical advances, the levels actually achieved through the ALARA principle have continued to fall. Generally, what may have started as advice and guidance has become frozen inflexibly into legislation and regulations.

In balancing the risks to man's survival, a totally fresh look at standards in radiation safety is needed. Consequential changes to safety laws and accepted working practice should be implemented with an eye to actual risk, not simply to placating supposed concern. There need to be upper limits on any single acute dose and on any chronic or repeated dose, accumulated within a repair time – conservatively suggested to be a month. Annual dose should not be used as a basis for regulation, and the use of collective dose, despite its administrative convenience, should be discontinued altogether. As set out in Chapter 7 suggested values for new limits, cautious but reflecting the known effect of repair and recovery times, are 100 millisievert for a single acute exposure and 100 millisievert per month for chronic or repeated doses. These values can be argued by factors of two, but in any event the limits should be several hundred times more relaxed than those currently applied. Interestingly, these proposed limits represent a relaxation by a modest factor of about six relative to the 1951 ICRP figures – a factor in line with what might be expected in view of the improved understanding of the mechanisms of radiobiology since 1951.

There remains the question of whether, *at some level*, there is still a small accumulation of irreparable reduced life expectancy as a result of radiation exposure. There seems to be little evidence for this at the present time – but we should put a limit on it. The clearest indication comes from the bone cancer data for the luminous dial painters showing a whole-of-life threshold of 10,000 millisievert.[59] Use of 5,000 millisievert as a general whole-of-life limit is suggested. This is to be compared with the 30,000 millisievert dose routinely given to healthy tissue over just 2 or 3 weeks in a single course of radiotherapy – in that case the lifelong risks are small and difficult to measure (see p. 119). The suggested limit is six times smaller and is taken over a whole lifetime rather than a month, and so may be seen as conservative.

In the future, as yet more is understood about the biological response to radiation, in particular about adaptive effects, there may be scope for further relaxation of these suggested limits: an acute limit, a short-term (monthly) limit and a whole-of-life limit.

As argued by the report of the French National Academies [22], a relaxed radiation safety regime would have benefits in diagnostic imaging, where current limits too easily discourage patients from accepting procedures that would be in their best interest.

In radiotherapy the position is quite different. As new technical solutions to the targeting of radiotherapy emerge, the dose to the tumour can be increased while the dose to peripheral tissue and organs is maintained at existing levels or reduced. The result will be a substantially improved success rate for tumour treatment, independent of any change in radiation safety levels.

Sixty years ago, when radiation safety first became a public concern, the looming threat was nuclear war rather than climate change. Then, the effects of radiation in biology were poorly

---

[59] The threshold reported by Rowland [40] and discussed in Chapter 7 is quoted in milligray. The large component of alpha radiation implies that this limit represents a larger number of millisievert. Again our interpretation is conservative.

understood and there was little information.[60] All that has now changed, and there is every reason not to exercise extreme caution. Nature seems content to use safety factors of about 10, depending on the risks and resource costs, but what margins should be used when considering radiation levels in the handling of nuclear fuel and waste? And, how do costs depend on such margins? Safety factors of a thousand are not affordable.

This is not a case for any relaxation in the engineering design of stable nuclear reactors. The use of several layers of independent control systems with different technologies as back-up is implemented on all modern reactors. Care is used to ensure that these are physically segregated and cannot be overridden by inexperienced operators, as at Chernobyl. Better monitoring and instrumentation ensures that it is known from the reactor control room exactly what is happening at all points inside and outside the reactor, which was not the case in the Three Mile Island incident. Reactor operating conditions are chosen for which any small increase in temperature causes a reduction in power production, by design and without the intervention of any external control. The Chernobyl reactor did not have such inherent stability. It is a matter for judgement as to which individual older plants do not measure up to these standards and when they should be replaced. Often it is the quality and reliability of welded pressure vessels and pipework, and the ability to test them, that is the problem.

New power stations

In March 2008 there were 439 reactors in 30 countries providing 16% of the world's electricity. Only 34 new power reactors were under construction in 11 countries, notably China, India, Japan, Korea and Russia, while in the 1980s a new reactor was coming on stream every 17 days [51]. With the increase in activity in

---

[60] Consequently efforts were made to obtain better data by exposing military personnel to low levels of radiation from nuclear tests. These experiments have been reported by the press with horror, but were understandable if ill-advised in the circumstances.

China and India it is possible that there could be a new 1 GWe reactor every 5 days by 2015. Currently, few reactors are under construction or on order for the US or Western Europe. In Germany, Austria, Australia and New Zealand public policy excludes the construction of new nuclear power stations, and the few that exist are due to be phased out.

The design of most reactors under construction, such as those in Finland and France, is based on pressurised light water as moderator and coolant. This design, which was described in outline on page 143, includes two walls of safety containment vessel and four layers of independent control systems, each capable of shutting the reactor down in case of an accident. To contain the consequences of the heat released following an emergency shutdown and cooling failure, popularly described as a *core meltdown*, there is a special isolated cooling area within the safety vessel. The net result is that the reactor design is very safe. Comparison may be made with the Chernobyl reactor, which had no containment vessel at all, none of the inherent automatic safety features and no meltdown protection.

Six different new reactor designs called Generation Four [52] are under development [53]. They may be realised on a time scale of 2020–2030. New features would improve thermal efficiency, fuel burn-up and waste management. Some use helium or lead cooling to allow operating temperatures of 500 to 1,000°C. Such a temperature would also facilitate direct production of hydrogen from water. On-site hydrogen production might provide efficient energy storage to cope with rapid fluctuations in demand. New ideas for closed fuel cycles, on-site reprocessing, actinide burn-up and the use of different fuels, could bring advantages to efficiency, cost, stability and control.

Another encouraging development is the Accelerator Driven Sub-critical Reactor (ADSR). This would use sub-critical fuel, that is not capable of sustaining a continuing chain reaction, such as natural thorium which is four times more plentiful than uranium. Fission is induced by neutrons generated within the reactor by an external proton accelerator [54]. Further neutrons are generated in the fission process but these do not survive in sufficient numbers to keep the reactor going and so the fission activity dies away as soon as the accelerator is turned off. The control is fail-safe and the reactor operates, in effect, as an energy amplifier. Actinide isotopes that are created can be burnt up so that radioactive waste is reduced. The design of a suitable accelerator is under development – such an accelerator would also have an important application as a source for ion-beam radiotherapy [33].

The nuclear industry has changed. Today it is concerned with international competition, commercial development consortia, international standards, designs and scrutiny. In earlier days there were nationally based development programmes, some of which had their eye on defence-related objectives. Some states still harbour such ambitions for their nuclear development, but their identity is well established and their programmes are not related to substituting for fossil fuel energy.

Fuel and politics

In the first instance nuclear fission relies on uranium, which is approximately as common as tin or zinc in the Earth's crust, occurring in most rocks and also the sea. Its distribution in commercially extractable concentrations is shown in Figure 24. The reserves are price-sensitive, but there is little doubt that these are sufficient to last mankind for a century or more, well into the era of nuclear fusion power.[61]

This distribution is politically rather equitable, compared with oil and gas whose known reserves are concentrated in areas of the globe with considerable political and cultural instability – the Middle East, the states of Central Asia and parts of Africa and South America. The ambition of developed countries to secure oil supplies has shaped world politics for a hundred years. The

---

[61] Successful exploration continues. A recent new find of 103,000 tons in Namibia is reported (2009) to be recoverable by open pit working at $61 per kg.

control by Russia of a large fraction of the European supply of gas is a present source of tension. The geopolitical distribution of uranium ore is more neutral, and a major switch to nuclear power would have a welcome pacifying influence on world affairs.

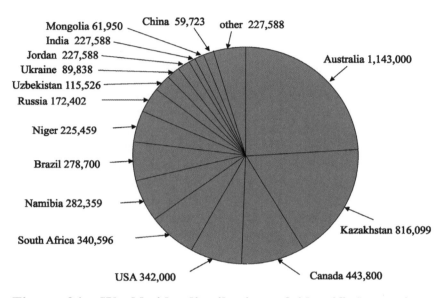

Figure 24   Worldwide distribution of identified uranium supplies (in tonnes of metal) recoverable at $130 per kg of uranium [55].

Another source of fission fuel is that provided by reprocessing. In addition, weapons-grade fuel may be degraded and used as a civil fuel source. Such a programme has been in operation by agreement between the USA and Russia since the end of the Cold War as part of the process of decommissioning nuclear weapons. Reprocessing plants were built initially to separate weapons-grade plutonium. As a result they have a sinister reputation and are closely monitored. But any separation activity releases the gas, krypton-53, into the atmosphere and this unique signature can be detected at distances of many kilometres [56]. The commercial use of reprocessing separates the re-useable actinides from the fission products, which has the environmental bonus of removing the long-lived components from the spent-fuel waste. Such plants currently exist in the UK, France, India, Japan and Russia.

Waste strategy

In the public perception the risk associated with nuclear waste is seen as the major barrier to an expanded programme of civil nuclear power. This concern is misplaced and a block in the way of solving a serious problem for mankind.

If the actinides have been removed from the waste by reprocessing, the remaining fission products may then be buried. After 500 years their activity will have decayed by a factor 100,000. At that level it becomes harmless – standard vitrification and deep burial in stable geology are certain to last for very much longer than that. By contrast the heavy metal waste from a fossil fuel plant is often poorly packaged, buried in shallow sites and remains hazardous indefinitely.

Not to reprocess makes no sense, either commercially or environmentally. If the waste is buried without reprocessing, the actinides remain radioactive on geological timescales, even after the fission products have decayed away. Concerns have been expressed that such buried waste might leak away and show up in the water supply. The story of the two billion year old Oklo Reactor [6, 7] discussed on page 52 suggests that this is unlikely if the burial site is chosen with any care at all. The storage life achieved at Oklo was many thousand times longer than any timescale of concern to mankind.

But what would happen in the unlikely event that radioactivity *did* leak from such a waste depository and contaminate a deep aquifer? The ground water would become very slightly radioactive over a long period. But this happens all the time with the natural radioactivity in the Earth which nobody buried carefully. It is curious that today, in spite of the widespread public concern about nuclear radiation, tourists still flock to health spas that boast radioactive ground water and hot baths heated by local radioactivity, that is geothermal energy. Their advertisements can be found on the Web. Here is one.

The Balneario de Fuente Amarga (Bitter Fountain) was established in 1867 and its waters declared for public use in 1871. It is located in the village of Tolox one hours drive inland from Marbella or Malaga at 360 meters above sea level at the entrance to the Sierra de la Nieves Natural Park and has clear air, a splendid warm climate, abundant water and green vegetation – a sheer delight in contrast to the pollution and stress of modern life.

The therapeutic properties of the water are: natural essential metals, nitrogenous, curative radioactivity, and calcium. Therapies offered include: Asthma in children, chronic bronchitis, bronchial asthma, emphysema, conjunctivitis, allergies, kidney stones, diuretic cures.

Therapy methods used include: drinking water, inhalations of natural gas, balsamic inhalations, natural gas aerosols, nasal douche, eye baths, mud spray treatments.

And here is another.

Milk River Bath is mineral spa in the South West corner of Clarendon Parish, Jamaica. Owned by the Government of Jamaica since its opening in 1794, it now has about 6 public baths and a hotel with about 20 bedrooms. The waters are 9 times as radioactive as those at Bath, England, and three times those at Karlvoy Vary, Czech Republic.

The 6 public baths are located in small private rooms off a seating area. The rooms are smartly tiled. Each can hold several people but the area for changing is really only suitable for one person at a time. The tepid water flows swiftly through the bath. The standard time for soaking is 15 minutes (for J$200 in 2006).

An adaptive response to the low radiation levels at these spas just might confer a real benefit by stimulating the general response mechanisms to cell damage, although this is speculative. At worst the radiation is just harmless and gives tourists a brief but welcome holiday away from their city homes.

If the actinides are removed from high level waste by reprocessing and then recycled as fuel, there is no need for large waste burial sites secure for longer than a few hundred years. Any deep dry mine should suffice as a depository. With Generation Four reactors or sub-critical reactors (ADSRs) the long-lived actinides can be burnt up to a considerable extent, so reducing the costly reprocessing of spent fuel as a separate stage.

Decommissioning

When a fission reactor reaches the end of its working life, it must be dismantled and the site cleared. If this is to be used for a replacement reactor, less stringent cleansing is justified, and decommissioning costs can be assessed on this basis. In fact it is very unusual to consider returning any heavy industrial site – refinery, steel plant or conventional power station – to agriculture or housing use.

The first step in decommissioning is to remove the fuel for reprocessing. This stage is much the same as happens during the operation of the working reactor, with the difference that the fuel is not then replaced. This takes about a year and removes 99% of the radioactive material.

The next stage takes longer. Any steel on the site containing cobalt that has been exposed to a neutron flux in the life of the reactor will have become contaminated by cobalt-60. This decays to nickel-60 with a half-life of 5.27 years and the emission of hard gamma rays.[62] As with all nuclear decays these cannot be simply *turned off* by any magic cleaning and the site remains hazardous. The most cost-effective procedure is to wait for 20 years, during which any activity drops to 5%, before dismantling and removing the last of the structural steel. By avoiding the use of cobalt steel as much as possible in new reactors, the duration and cost of future decommissioning will be reduced. During this stage any material containing long-lived

---

[62] On page 135 it was stated that materials are very rarely made radioactive by radiation *except* by exposure to neutrons, as in this case.

actinides is removed and buried as low or intermediate level waste.

In the final stage after 20 years any remaining fission products on the ground of the cleared site are left to decay. The caesium and strontium are the longest lived, with half-lives of 30 years. If left fallow for 150 years or more, the site would become effectively contamination free, but it is more sensible to re-use it earlier, for instance for suitable industrial storage. Early reactors were not built with decommissioning in mind, but new designs with less cobalt steel and the increased use of robotic handling will ease the task. Naturally, with a more relaxed tolerance of ionising radiation, the whole decommissioning process should become substantially quicker and cheaper – more like the decommissioning of a coal-fired power station for which no special provision is made.

No report has been found of any loss of life in the past 60 years due to radiation in the building, operation, fuel handling, waste disposal or decommissioning of a nuclear power reactor anywhere in Europe or the USA.

Proliferation and terrorism

Who is threatened and who would use nuclear weapons? No one side is trusted by the other in a war of fear – the same war of nerves and propaganda as was played out on the battlefields of ancient history. The difference is that in the modern version of this game of cards, no card is actually played – anyway, not in the past 60 years. Yet the war may still be won when the confidence of one side collapses, as happened at the end of the Cold War when the Soviet Union gave up the struggle. The radiation and the nuclear blast never actually came on stage – they remained virtual, a threat.

High purity uranium enrichment and the production of pure plutonium are indicative of weapon production. These are well monitored by IAEA and this has prevented the proliferation of weapons in the past, at least in many cases. However, when weapons production is detected, political decisiveness is required to act on this information – but who should act? This seems to be a weak point. As a result, some nations have acquired a military nuclear capability and some have not – and the number who have rises slowly. Some nations behave responsibly in world affairs and have the stability needed to be custodians of weapon technology, and some do not. But technical and economic strength are not related to responsible behaviour. Narrow religious fundamentalism and local self-interest seem to drive the actions of nuclear and non-nuclear states alike. The possession of military might is no guarantee against harmful ideological or religious political control. It is clear that firm international control of enrichment and reprocessing plant needs to be enforced for the common good [57].

But the fear generated by the word *radiation* and the description *nuclear* in the minds of the public and press, can be exploited by governments and terrorists. For terrorists and small rogue states the task of building a viable bomb based on a nuclear explosive is difficult. However, any form of *dirty bomb* is a simple and credible threat, and this could be a conventional chemical explosive device that contaminates a local area by dispersing radioactive material. Or the threat might be to crash an airliner into a nuclear power plant. Such a strike on a modern plant would be quite ineffective, as the reactor containment vessel is massive and designed to withstand such exceptional stresses in any case. In the unlikely event that the vessel was breached, the worst that could happen is a spillage of radioactive fuel, but without the initial surge of heat that initiated the explosion at Chernobyl. As a result, any release of radioactivity would be local, and there would be no fallout without the exceptional heat to propel radioactivity high into the atmosphere. In short, a nuclear power station would be a very poor choice of target for an ambitious terrorist. But as a threat it would be very effective, unless a sizeable fraction of the population was sufficiently educated to see through the threat.

The message of the preceding chapters is that any threat or blackmail based on radioactive spillage ought to be treated as rather impotent, for, if carried through, the effects would be local and modest for all but a few. The only leverage of any threat would depend on the unbridled imagination of the public and press – and the possibility of ensuing popular panic. If people were better informed and reassured, the terrorists would have to change their minds and choose, instead, a genuinely more effective method, such as a 9/11 or a biochemical attack. So the best defence against a dirty nuclear bomb is public education with a more realistic radiation safety regime – in fact, a policy that simply devalues the currency of any such blackmail.

Fusion power

The long-term solution to the need for large scale energy supply is nuclear fusion power. This has been a prospect for many years but has now progressed to the point where it may be expected in a generation or two, well within the life of the latest fission power stations [45, 58].

The first task has been to realise the very high temperature required for long enough and with a density sufficient to ignite fusion. There are several ways to do this, but the current favourite is the toroidal tokamak. Ignition has now been demonstrated, but much more development is required to build a reliable power plant.

Fusion power will be safer and cleaner than fission power. Unlike in weaponry where fission is needed as a detonator for a fusion explosion, there is no role at all for nuclear fission in a fusion reactor. The principal waste product is helium, which is arguably the safest and most innocuous material on Earth. The reaction that produces the energy is between tritium and deuterium, that is

hydrogen-3 + hydrogen-2 → helium-4 + neutron.

The neutron which carries away most of the energy is then moderated by a lithium blanket surrounding the reactor before being absorbed by the reaction

neutron + lithium-6 → helium-4 + hydrogen-3.
Cooling circuits in the blanket deliver the energy to the turbines. Meanwhile the tritium is regenerated. The only input is lithium and deuterium.

Lithium is plentiful in the Earth's crust (50 parts per million). It has been calculated that the lithium in a used laptop battery and the deuterium in half a bath of water contain enough fuel to provide the energy requirements of a UK resident for 30 years [45]. There is no long-lived radioactivity involved and the production of waste by-products is on a tiny scale. Tritium is very weakly radioactive with a 12-year half life, but there is no net production of it and the required inventory is small. In a fission reactor at any time there is enough unburnt fuel to power it for more than a year, and that is why control and stability are so important. But in a fusion reactor this is not so. Only a minute mass of fuel is loaded at any time and power production can be switched off at short notice by cutting the fuel supply, as in a petrol or diesel engine. There is no continuing energy release after shutdown, as there is in a fission reactor. There can be no widespread environmental consequences of an accident because the stored energy is less than in a fossil fuel plant. Like a fission reactor, a fusion power source is physically large with a high steady energy output, which could be linked to desalination or hydrogen production as well as electricity generation and local use of waste heat.

To realise such power plants, what is now required is further technical investment and development, largely in materials technology. This is the task for the International Thermonuclear Experimental Reactor (ITER) project that is now under construction in the South of France. No doubt there will be lessons to learn. Some of these may involve expensive setbacks, but they will not be dangerous on a global scale. No doubt there will be accidents – even some loss of life – on a local scale, as there is in any demanding human endeavour. But the record of the last 50 years in the nuclear industry suggests that when these occur they will be due to familiar mechanical and chemical hazards like scaffolding, ladders, fire and electrical faults.

Costs and the economy

Can these substantial developments in nuclear and fusion power be afforded? The world needs economic stimulus in a period of recession, as much as it needs a scientifically viable approach to climate change. It seems likely that those countries and those businesses that can put these two together will prosper, although the current safety culture, planning laws and public perception of radiation obstruct this objective.

The current cost of nuclear power is amplified by radiation safety regulations and the voice of public concern. Every element of provision for public safety, worker protection and working practices raises costs. This is appropriate if those provisions are actually necessary. But if, as seems likely, many are not, the extra financial yoke that this places on the future of nuclear power may have serious avoidable consequences for civilisation.

The conditions in the waste reprocessing plant at Sellafield, UK serve as an example. In the storage hall where thousands of tons of recently vitrified waste are cooled awaiting burial in decades to come, the radiation level in the working area is less than 1 microsievert per hour, that is about 0.8 millisievert per month. This may be compared with the 30,000 millisievert per month received by the healthy tissue of a radiotherapy patient, and the figure of 100 millisievert per month suggested in Chapter7 as an appropriate safe limit – not that anyone would live for 24 hours a day, 7 days a week in such a hall. It is truly impressive that such safety levels are maintained, but this has been achieved at great cost and the money is not well spent.

With a major relaxation in the current value of radiation safety limits and improved public understanding, the competitive position of nuclear power would be transformed. The stability and control of any power plant should remain the prime consideration, but the cost implications of a relaxation on other parts of nuclear power plant construction, operation and decommissioning would be significant. The handling, transport and security of fuel – as well as the cooling, storage, recycling and disposal of spent fuel – would still require measures of security and remote handling, but would be cheaper, faster and altogether less conservative.

The cost of decommissioning a plant at the end of its life should not be the major item that it is popularly supposed to be. The IAEA reported in 1990 that [59]

> *decommissioning was technologically feasible, the waste volumes were manageable, and that decommissioning costs had a very small impact on the electricity generation costs. On an annual basis, the funding required (costs) for decommissioning of a large commercial reactor would be 2%-5% of electricity generation costs.*

This report concerned the older plants that were not designed with decommissioning in mind. Since 1990 the working lives of many plants have been extended from 25 to 40, even to 60, years, and this spreads the capital cost. Modern plants with their improved design and working life of 60 years should have small decommissioning costs, even before the impact of reconsidered radiation limits. There is no justification for accounting the cost of decommissioning a nuclear plant any differently than a non-nuclear plant. The current tendency is to talk up the cost of decommissioning in the name of being responsible [60]. It is irresponsible to increase notional costs in the absence of related uncertainties.

The entire uranium and plutonium nuclear technology was designed and built from the basic physics upward in 3 or 4 years in the early 1940s. Today, internationally approved power station designs exist and, if mankind is serious in his reaction to climate change, such power stations could be constructed far more quickly than is supposed. The main causes of delay are planning and public safety concerns – with renewed public goodwill these could be accelerated substantially. Two other causes of delay are foundry capacity and manpower. There is a lack of capacity to produce significant numbers of the large high quality stainless steel castings required – but recent reports suggest that this is being addressed. In the decades in which nuclear technology was out of fashion, the number of young people studying it declined. Today, in many countries the number of nuclear physicists and engineers is low and it will take time and effort to build up the required skills base and expertise. This will limit the rate at which new plants can be built and brought on stream. One real lesson that can be learnt from the Chernobyl accident is that the manpower required to operate, as well as to build, a nuclear power station must be properly trained and responsible. But this can be achieved. In 1940 there was no nuclear skills base at all, for the whole technology was new. Nevertheless, with determination the job was done in 4 or 5 years by importing and educating bright skilled people from other areas. Of course, any reckoning of the number of skilled physicists and engineers required should be reduced by reconsidering how many need to be engaged on aspects of safety.

Fresh water and food

There are further contributions that radiation and nuclear power can bring to help the environment.

As described in Chapter 2, to provide more fresh water from sea water on a large scale, desalination plants with abundant energy supplies are needed. Otherwise, major water shortages are expected in many parts of the world, as aquifers become exhausted and the climate changes. A nuclear power plant can provide this energy efficiently with sea water cooling and the desalination plant on the same site.

Most food produced never reaches the table. It is eaten by pests, or deteriorates and is thrown away. Its storage life can be extended by energy-consuming refrigeration, but an alternative method is sterilisation by ionising radiation. Food irradiation is recommended as completely safe by the World Health Organization [61] and is used in many countries. Extraordinarily, it is not permitted in most developed countries. Most western consumers know nothing about it and so, if asked, would reject it simply on account of its association with radiation.

The sterilisation process uses very high doses of gamma rays from a cobalt-60 source, more than 50,000 gray, that is 5×10^7 millisievert. These gamma rays (1.3 MeV) are not energetic enough to excite any nuclei and it is not possible for them to make the food radioactive. However, it is sufficient to kill all microbes through the biological damage caused. The effect on the food itself is like pasteurisation, which causes cell death by heating – cooking is another similar process, that is trusted as normal and safe because it is familiar. Exceptionally, there are foods for which pasteurisation or irradiation have a slight effect on texture or flavour, and then irradiation is not considered suitable. Cooking is not suitable for all foods either, but that is a more extreme treatment. But some governments seem frightened to explain that food irradiation would be beneficial to their citizenry, and such lack of leadership itself gives cause for concern.

Such intense gamma ray sources have other important beneficial uses. In hospitals, exposures similar to those for food irradiation are used for the sterilisation of supplies, including dressings and surgical instruments. These powerful sources of ionising radiation are used also in industry for the non-destructive quality control of materials by detecting internal cracks and voids. As a result most materials do not break or fail, as was the case in earlier decades.

Education and understanding

There is a need to keep track of these intense sources. Accidents happen when they get misplaced, and this underlines the importance of long-term record keeping, improved public education about radiation, and increased availability of radiation monitors. These deserve attention at the same time as the suggested overall relaxation of radiation safety levels. More generally, the operation of a safe civil nuclear power programme in any society presupposes a certain level of political stability and education. Otherwise, the required indigenous skills base and atmosphere of personal, as well as collective, responsibility are not likely to be maintained.

The links between safety, education and personal responsibility are crucial in every society, developed and developing. The political climate of the Cold War encouraged collective rather than individual scientific initiative and responsibility, as lamented by President Eisenhower in his prescient speech, delivered as he was leaving office in 1961. He was concerned for the voice of the alert individual citizen and, particularly, the freedom of universities.

> *In the councils of government, we must guard against the acquisition of unwarranted influence, whether sought or unsought, by the military-industrial complex. The potential for the disastrous rise of misplaced power exists and will persist....*
>
> *Only an alert and knowledgeable citizenry can compel the proper meshing of the huge industrial and military machinery of defense with our peaceful methods and goals, so that security and liberty may prosper together....*
>
> *In this revolution, research has become central; it also becomes more formalized, complex, and costly. A steadily increasing share is conducted for, by, or at the direction of, the Federal government. Today, the solitary inventor, tinkering in his shop, has been overshadowed by task forces of scientists in laboratories and testing fields. In the same fashion, the free university, historically the fountainhead of free ideas and scientific discovery, has experienced a revolution in the conduct of research. Partly because of the huge costs involved, a government contract becomes virtually a substitute for intellectual curiosity. For every old blackboard there are now hundreds of new electronic computers. The prospect of domination of the nation's scholars by Federal*

employment, project allocations, and the power of money is ever present and is gravely to be regarded. ...

It is the task of statesmanship to mold, to balance, and to integrate these and other forces, new and old, within the principles of our democratic system – ever aiming toward the supreme goals of our free society.

Valedictory Speech (part), Dwight D. Eisenhower, 1961

The threats which he described did not disappear at the end of the Cold War. By then the collective machine that he identified had become increasingly international – and the safety industry was a part of that. But now the attitude to safety should change – it is imperative that it be recast to match the new threats to the world.

There is a further educational danger that has been added by the top-down centralised agenda that Eisenhower described. Organisation, especially of large-scale activities, is more manageable when separated into pieces. The temptation is to extend this from management to understanding, and to delegate fragments of a problem to experts. This may be efficient once the problem is structured correctly, but it means that few people, if any, get to appreciate and see the whole. Therefore, the most glaring errors can get glossed over and ignored. This, it would seem, is what has happened in the matter of the effects of radiation. In the recent past, education has been permitted to develop by encouraging such compartmentalisation. So the lesson needs to be learnt and the message needs to go out, that the benefits of specialisation are limited, and that learning in modules is often injurious to the achievement of a real understanding of the whole. The need is for generalists, both deep and broad, especially in the sciences. When expertise is used, it should be interrogated and spread around to inform the whole, not accepted blindly. Thinking by delegation – off-loading tasks of understanding to consultants – does not deliver the right answer. Learning ourselves from our own experiences, and from one another, is hard work, but we need to hand a broad scientific knowledge on to our children and grandchildren. The alternative may be an environmental dark age from which there is no simple escape. Specifically, mankind must use his wits if he is to survive climate change. In the past he closed his mind to nuclear solutions, and this was a mistake because civil nuclear technology is the only possible approach that is sufficient to cut the main driver of escalating climate change. We need it to maintain the world economy while avoiding the discontent and unrest that could lead to dischord and war on a world scale.

Chapter 11 Summary of Conclusions

Risks to health associated with ionising radiation have been overestimated by a wide margin. This conclusion has been reached bringing together three sources of scientific information: firstly a century of clinical experience of radiotherapy; secondly the current knowledge of radiobiology based on laboratory studies; thirdly the analysis of the long-term health records of large populations of people exposed to radiation, either as a single (acute) dose or as a continuing (chronic) one. The result is that new safety levels for human radiation exposures are suggested: 100 millisievert in a single dose; 100 millisievert in total in any month; 5,000 millisievert as a total whole-of-life exposure. These figures are conservative, and may be debatable within factors of two, but not ten.

There are three reasons why existing radiation safety standards have been set at levels that are typically a thousand times more cautious: firstly the association in the public mind of radiation with the dangers of nuclear weapons; secondly the advice of authorities, set up with a narrow remit to minimise public exposure to radiation and to satisfy the public aspiration for safety and reassurance; thirdly the lack of available firm scientific evidence and understanding in earlier decades. During the Cold War era there were good political reasons not to minimise the health legacy of a nuclear war, but this association is now engrained in the general consciousness. In their physical destructive power nuclear weapons are especially dangerous. But, when the initial blast with its flash of ionising radiation and heat has gone, the residual radioactivity and fallout have a much smaller impact on human health than was supposed in the past. The underlying idea that a radiation dose, however small, leaves an indelible mark on health is not supportable. The evidence that workers exposed to radiation have 15–20% lower mortality from cancer before age 85 suggests that low doses of radiation might be beneficial.

New dangers are now evident. These are more global and threatening than any local nuclear incident, and arise from changes in the Earth's atmosphere, triggered by the continuing use of fossil fuels. Although many initiatives are possible in response, the only large-scale solution is a major switch to nuclear power for electricity generation and the supply of additional fresh water. For this to happen rapidly, cheaply and without disruption, the public perception of ionising radiation needs to be turned around, and substantial changes in regulations and working practices, based on new safety levels, determined afresh. For the future, improved biological understanding may be able to justify relaxing safety levels still further, and legislation and working practices should be drawn up, allowing for this possibility. Such a relaxation of safety levels by factors of about a thousand means that current concerns, such as waste, decommissioning, radiation health, terrorism and costs, can be seen in a better light.

This is a most positive conclusion. But are we able and ready to reconsider our views, and then act fast enough to lessen the impending change in climate?

Further Reading and References

A readable description of Chernobyl today, *Wormwood Forest, a natural history of Chernobyl* by Mary Mycio, together with the pictures on her website [14].

An accessible but more student-oriented account of the science, *Radiation and Health* by T. Henriksen and H. D. Maillie [16].

More on the science of nuclear and medical physics, *Fundamental Physics for Probing and Imaging* by Wade Allison, [4].

An article on the science of the power and influence of suggestion on life and health *The science of voodoo* by Helen Pilcher [2].

More on the science of energy production *Energy Science* by J. Andrews and N. Jelley, Oxford University Press (2007).

References

More recent information and updates are given on the associated website at http://www.radiationandreason.com

[1] Wilmott, P (2000). *The use, misuse and abuse of mathematics in finance*. Philosophical Transactions of the Royal Society. A358:63–73. http://www.jstor.org/pss/2666776 [accessed 15 February 2009].

[2] Pilcher, H (2009).*The science of voodoo: when mind attacks body*. New Scientist. May 2009. http://www.newscientist.com/article/m g20227081.100-the-science-of-voodoo-when-mind-attacks-body.html [accessed 12 August 2009],

[3] Deutsch, D. (1997). *The Fabric of Reality* Penguin.

[4] Allison, W. (2006) *Fundamental Physics for Probing and Imaging*. Oxford University Press.

[5] Watson, S J et al. (2005) *Ionising Radiation Exposure of the UK Population: 2005 Review.* UK Health Protection Agency, Report RPD-001.

[6] Wikipedia (2009). *Natural Nuclear Fission Reactor* http://en.wikipedia.org/wiki/Natural_nuclear_fission_reactor [accessed 18 May 2009].

[7] Meshik, A P. (2005) *The Workings of an Ancient Nuclear Reactor.* Scientific American, Nov 2005, 293:56–63.

[8] IAEA (1996) *International Basic Safety Standards for Protection against Ionizing Radiation and for the Safety of Radiation Sources 115.* The International Atomic Energy Agency. http://www.pub.iaea.org/MTCD/publications/PDF/_SS-115-Web/Pub996_web-1a.pdf [accessed 10 February 2009, but apparently deleted shortly thereafter].

[9] WHO (2004) *Malaria and HIV/AIDS Interactions and Implications* Conclusions of a technical consultation convened by WHO. http://www.emro.who.int/aiecf/web26.pdf [accessed 12 February 2009].

[10] FHWA (2007) *Press Release: call on States to Immediately Inspect All Steel Arch Truss Bridges.* Federal Highway Administration, 2 August 2007. http://www.fhwa.dot.gov/pressroom/fhwa0712.htm [accessed 21 February 2009].

[11] OECD (2002) *Chernobyl: Assessment of Radiological and Health Impacts.* Report 3508, OECD/National Energy Agency, Paris. http://www.nea.fr/html/rp/chernobyl/welcome.html [accessed 11 February 2009].

[12] IAEA (2006) *Chernobyl's Legacy.* International Atomic Energy Agency. http://www.iaea.org/Publications/Booklets/Chernobyl/chernobyl.pdf [accessed 14 February 2009].

[13] WHO (2006) *Health effects of the Chernobyl accident and Special Health Care Programmes.* Report of the UN Chernobyl Forum, World Health Organization. http://whqlibdoc.who.int/publications/2006/9241594179_eng.pdf [accessed 5 July 2009].

[14] Mycio, M (2005). *Wormwood Forest, a natural history of Chernobyl.* Joseph Henry Press. http://www.chernobyl.in.ua [accessed 10 February 2009].

[15] BBC (2006) *Nuclear Nightmares*. BBC Horizon documentary, 13 July 2006. A related BBC website can be found at http://news.bbc .co.uk/1/hi/sci/tech/5173310.stm [accessed 5 July 2009].

[16] Henriksen, T, and Maillie, H D. (2003) *Radiation & Health*. Taylor & Francis.

[17] Merkle, W. (1983) *Statistical methods in regression and calibration analysis of chromosome aberration data*. Radiation and Environmental Biophysics. 21:217–233. http://www.springerlink .com/content/q84x2p284r380187/ [accessed 13 February 2009].

[18] Nakamura, N. et al (1998) *A close correlation between electron spin resonance (ESR) dosimetry from tooth enamel and cytogenetic dosimetry from lymphocytes of Hiroshima atomic-bomb survivors*. International Journal of Radiation Biology, 73:619–627. http://cat.inist .fr/?aModele =afficheN&cpsidt=2338882 [accessed 13 February 2009].

[19] Preston, Dale L. et al (2004) *Effect of Recent Changes in Atomic Bomb Survivor Dosimetry on Cancer Mortality Risk Estimates*. Radiation Research. 162: 377–389. http://www.bioone.org/doi/abs /10.1667/RR3232 [accessed 6 February 2009].

[20] Shimizu, Y. et al (1999) *Studies of the Mortality of Atomic Bomb Survivors. Report 12, Part II. Noncancer Mortality: 1950–1990*. Radiation Research. 152: 374–389. http://www.jstor.org/pss/3580222 [accessed 27 February 2009].

[21] Tubiana, M. and Aurengo, A. (2005) *Dose-effect relationships and estimation of the carcinogenic effects of low doses of ionizing radiation*. Joint Report of the Academie des Sciences (Paris) and the Academie Nationale de Medecine. http://www.academie-sciences.fr /publications/rapports/pdf/dose_effet_07_04_05.pdf [accessed 25 May 2009].

[22] Tubiana, M and Aurengo, A. (2006) *Dose-effect relationships and estimation of the carcinogenic effects of low doses of ionizing radiation*. Joint Report of the Academie des Sciences (Paris) and the Academie Nationale de Medecine. International Journal of Low Radiation. 2:135–153. http://www.ingentaconnect.com/content/ind /ijlr/2006/00000002/F0020003/art00001 [accessed 11 February 2009].

[23] NRPB (2001) *Stable Iodine Prophylaxis.* Recommendations of the 2nd UK Working Group on Stable Iodine Prophylaxis, National Radiological Protection Board. http://www.hpa.org.uk/webc /HPAwebFile/HPAweb_C/1194947336017 [accessed 14 March 2009].

[24] Windscale (2007). *The Windscale reactor accident—50 years on.* (Editorial) Journal of Radiological Protection. 27:211–215. http://www.iop.org/EJ/article/0952-4746/13/4/001/jr930401.pdf [accessed 11 February 2009].

[25] Cardis, E. et al. (2005) *Risk of Thyroid Cancer after exposure to iodine-131 in childhood,* Journal of the National Cancer Institute 97(10) 724–732. http://jnci.oxfordjournals.org/cgi/content/short/97/ 10/724 [accessed 21 February 2009].

[26] Boice, J D. (2005) *Radiation-induced Thyroid Cancer – What's New?* Editorial, Journal of the National Cancer Institute 97(10):703– 32. http://jnci.oxfordjournals.org/cgi/content/full/97/10/703 [accessed 11 February 2009].

[27] ICRP (2007) *Report 103: 2007 Recommendations.* International Commission for Radiological Protection. http://www.icrp.org [accessed 10 February 2009].

[28] Dagens Nyheter (2002). Article published in the major Stockholm morning paper on 24 April by Swedish Radiation Protection Authority. An English translation, http://www.radiationandreason.com/uploads /dagens_nyheter_C3D.pdf.

[29] Simmons, J A. and Watt, D E. (1999) *Radiation Protection Dosimetry, A Radical Reappraisal.* Medical Physics Publishing, Madison, Wisconsin.

[30] RCR (2006) *Radiotherapy Dose Fractionation.* Royal College of Radiologists. http://rcr.ac.uk/docs/oncology/pdf/Dose-Fractionation_Fi nal.pdf [accessed 11 February 2009].

[31] Roychoudhuri, R. et al (2007) *Increased cardiovascular mortality more than fifteen years after radiotherapy for breast cancer: a population-based study.* BioMed Central Cancer, 7: 9. http://www .ncbi.nlm.nih.gov/pubmed/17224064. [accessed 27 February 2009].

[32] GSI (2005). *Cancer Therapy with Ion Beams.* GSI, Darmstadt. http://www.gsi.de/portrait/Broschueren/Therapie/Krebstherapie_e.html [accessed 13 February 2009].

[33] BASROC (2006) *UK Hadron Therapy Accelerator Group.* http://www.basroc.org.uk/documentation.htm [accessed 21 February 2009].

[34] Darby, S. et al. (2005) *Radon in homes and risk of lung cancer: collaborative analysis of individual data from 13 European case-control studies.* British Medical Journal 2005; 330, 223–228. http://www.bmj.com/cgi/content/full/330/7485/223 [accessed 12 February 2009].

[35] Darby, S et al. (2006) *Residential radon and lung cancer, the risk of lung cancer* Scandinavian Journal of Work, Environment and Health 2006;32 supplement 1. http://www.sjweh.fi/order_supplement.php [accessed 11 February 2009].

[36] WHO (2006) *Radon and Cancer.* World Health Organization http://www.who.int/mediacentre/factsheets/fs291/en/index.html [accessed 11 February 2009].

[37] Berrington et al (2001) *100 years of observation on British radiologists: mortality from cancer and other diseases, 1897–1997.* British Journal of Radiology, 74 (2001), 507–519. http://bjr.birjournals.org/cgi/content/full/74/882/507 [accessed 25 May 2009].

[38] Muirhead, C R et al (2009). *Mortality and cancer incidence following occupational radiation exposure: third analysis of the National Registry for Radiation Workers.* British Journal of Cancer, 100, 206–212. http://www.nature.com/bjc/journal/v100/n1/full/6604825a.html [accessed 3rd April 2009].

[39] Simmons, J A. (2008) *Response to 'Commentary: What Can Epidemiology Tell us about Risks at Low Doses?'* Radiation Research. 170: 139–141. http://www.bioone.org/doi/abs/10.1667/RR1391a.1 [accessed 25 May 2009].

[40] Rowland, R.E. et al (1997) *Bone sarcoma in humans induced by radium: A threshold response?* Radioprotection 32: C1-331–C1-338.

[41] Pollycove, M and Feinendegen, L E (2008) *Low-dose radioimmuno-therapy of cancer*. Human Experimental Toxicology. 2008; 27: 169–175.   http://het.sagepub.com/cgi/reprint/27/2/169 [accessed 27 February 2009].

[42] BEIR VII (2005) *Health Risks from Exposure to Low Levels of Ionizing Radiation: BEIR VII – Phase 2*. The National Academies Press. http://www.nap.edu/catalog/11340.html [accessed 23rd March 2009].

[43] UNSCEAR (1994). *Sources and Effects of Ionizing Radiation.* Report to UN General Assembly http://www.unscear.org/unscear/en/publications/1994.html [accessed 10 April 2009].

[44] Mitchell, R E J. and Boreham, D R (2000). *Radiation Protection in the World of Modern Radiobiology: Time for A New Approach.* International Radiation Protection Association, Hiroshima, Japan, 15–19 May 2000.   http://www.radscihealth.org/rsh/docs/Mitchel.html [accessed 12 February 2009].

[45] Llewellyn-Smith, C. (2006) *The Potential Role of Fusion in 2100.* Presentation to the Royal Academy of Engineering, 8 May 2006. http://www.raeng.org.uk/policy/reports/pdf/energy_2100/Llewellyn_Smith.pdf [accessed 14 February 2009].

[46] World Nuclear Association (1999). *Conversion and Enrichment.* http://www.world-nuclear.org/how/enrichment.html [accessed 11 February 2009].

[47] Areva (2009) *The 1600+ MWe Reactor.* Areva Company. http://www.epr-reactor.co.uk/scripts/ssmod/publigen/content/templates/show.asp?P=93&L=EN [accessed 2 September 2009].

[48] Royal Society (2001) *The health effects of depleted uranium munitions.* http://royalsociety.org/displaypagedoc.asp?id=11496 [accessed 10 April 2009].

[49] World Nuclear Association (2006) *Waste.* http://www.world-nuclear.org/education/wast.htm [accessed 4 April 2009].

[50] Tubiana, M. et al. (2006) *Recent reports on the effect of low doses of ionizing radiation and its dose–effect relationship* Radiation and Environmental Biophysics 2006 44:245. http://www.springerlink.com/content/yg4m73410313447j/ [accessed 25 May 2009].

[51] World Nuclear Association (2008) *Plans for New Nuclear Reactors Worldwide.* http://www.world-nuclear.org/info/inf17.html [accessed 11 February 2009].

[52] GenerationIV (2009) *Generation IV 2008 Annual Report.* Gen-IV International Forum. http://www.gen-4.org/PDFs/GIF_2008_Annual _Report.pdf [accessed 6 April 2009].

[53] World Nuclear Association (2008) *Generation IV Nuclear Reactors.* http://www.world-nuclear.org/info/inf77.html [accessed 11 February 2009].

[54] ThorEA (2009) *Thorium energy amplifiers.* http://www2.hud.ac.uk/news/2009news/05_thorea.php [accessed 2 September 2009]..

[55] World Nuclear Association (2008) *Supply of Uranium.* http:// www.world-nuclear.org/info/inf75.html [accessed 27 February 2009.

[56] Kalinowski, M B. et al. (2004) *Conclusions on plutonium separation from atmospheric krypton-85 measured at various distances.* Journal of Environmental Radioactivity 2004. 73;2:203– 222. http://cat.inist.fr/?aModele=afficheN&cpsidt=15580560 [accessed 11 February 2009].

[57] El Baradei, M. (2009) *A Recipe for Survival.* International Herald Tribune, 16 February, 2009. http://www.iaea.org/NewsCenter _/Transcripts/2009/iht160209.html [accessed 2 September 2009].

[58] World Nuclear Association (2007) *Nuclear Fusion Power.* http:// www.world-nuclear.org/info/inf66.html [accessed 29 March 2009].

[59] IAEA (1990) *Costs of Decommissioning Nuclear Power Plants.* International Atomic Energy Agency. http://www.iaea.org/ Publications/Magazines/ Bulletin/Bull323/32304783942.pdf [accessed 23 February 2009].

[60] BERR (2006) *Reactor Decommissioning.* Informal report prepared for the UK Goverment by Ernst and Young. http://www.berr.gov.uk/files/file36327.pdf [accessed 29 March 2009].

[61] WHO (1997) *High-dose irradiation: wholesomeness of food irradiated with doses above 10 KGy.* A joint FAO/IAEA/WHO study group. World Health Organization. http://www.who.int/foodsafety/pub lications/fs_management/ irradiation/en/ [accessed 11 February 2009].

Index